THE PLIGHT OF THE PENGUIN

The ~~Flight~~ *Plight* of the Penguin

Lloyd Spencer Davis

Longacre Press

TO DANIEL AND KELSEY:

The best brood a guy could ever have.

ISBN 1 877135 56 9

First published by Longacre Press, 2001.
9 Dowling Street, Dunedin, New Zealand.

FRONT COVER PHOTO:
An Adelie penguin negotiates blocks of ice built up over winter at the margin of the sea and the land.
(Photo: Lloyd Spencer Davis)

ACKNOWLEDGEMENTS

The short quotations used at the beginning of each chapter are acknowledged as follows:

'History' reproduced with permission by Mushroom Music Publishing. Writer's credit: Neil Finn.

'Lola' ©1970 Mondvies Music Inc. Used by permission of Belinda Music (Australia) Pty Ltd. Writer's credit: Ray Davies. (All rights reserved)

'Love the One You're With' – writer's credit: Stephen Stills, and 'Romeo and Juliet' – writer's credit: Mark Knopfler. Universal Music. Every reasonable attempt was made to find copyright owners of both songs.

'Wish You Were Here' reproduced by kind permission of Warner/Chappell Music Australia Pty Ltd. Writer's credit: Roger Waters/David Gilmour. (Unauthorised reproduction is illegal)

* * *

This book owes its life to Barbara Larson. She encouraged me to write it and then helped nurture it through a prolonged adolescence. I am grateful to Barbara and all those at Longacre Press for being both cheerleader and coach to me. A special word of gratitude goes to Jenny Cooper for her sympathetic design. The photographs are an integral part of the design and I have been privileged to work with graduate students who share a love of photography and penguins. It is a huge pleasure to include images from some of them here (Corey Bradshaw, Gordon Court, Richard Cuthbert, Melanie Massaro, Martin Renner, Philip Seddon and Yolanda van Heezik) along with those from friends I have worked with (Dee Boersma, John Darby and Ewan Fordyce). Long-time friend, Sarah Wroot, has somehow managed to turn my crude ideas into delightful illustrations. The multi-talented, Emmy award-winning friend Ian McGee generously drew the cartoon of Brezhnev for nothing more than a bottle of wine. Colin Tudge, one of the world's busiest writers, kindly interrupted a rare break to write the foreword from a beach somewhere in Malta. And, finally, I thank Frances for giving me the space to follow my dreams.

Book and cover design by Jenny Cooper. Illustrations by Sarah Wroot. Printed by Everbest Printing Company Ltd, China.

CONTENTS

Foreword

by Colin Tudge

THIS BOOK is excellent, everything it should be: a scampering read, fast and funny; excellent natural history, observed first hand; and all underpinned by the deep ideas of modern biology, from evolutionary theory to behavioural ecology to the biophysics of underwater flight and temperature control. The photographs are wondrous too, to match their subject, and mostly taken by the author.

Penguins may seem easy enough to study, as they waddle up the beaches on islands and continents from the Equator through the subtropics and so on down to the ice of Antarctica. I saw my first wild penguins – Yellow-eyed – on a wide sandy beach in New Zealand. They sidled with feigned nonchalance between the sealions to the left of them and the fur seals to the right, perfectly equidistant from both, then scuttled as fast as their stumpy legs would carry them to their roosts in the dunes beyond.

But all natural history is much harder than it seems for even when the subjects are conspicuous it is hard to make sense of what you see, and penguins confuse in all conceivable ways. Truly to make sense of what wild creatures are up to takes hours and hours and months and months of patient recording, which is none too easy if, like Emperors, the subjects spend their winters on Antarctic ice at minus 60 degrees. But it also takes a particular mindset that is very difficult to maintain. For as Charles Darwin said (he, the greatest field naturalist of all), you cannot understand anything you see in the wild unless you first have an idea of what to expect: a hypothesis. If you just apply what Claude Monet called 'the innocent eye', you will perceive nothing. But if your hypothesis is too rigid, then everything you see will be pressed into your preconception, and your ideas will never expand. The old naturalists thought penguins mated for life and looked after the chicks indiscriminately because, in effect, they assumed that penguins must be as sweet by nature as they are quaint to look at. It took modern theory to perceive that like every other creature they are tough little survival machines that cannot afford just to be cuddly.

As survival machines, however, they are particularly wonderful: as Lloyd Spencer Davis says, they are bona-fide, copper-bottomed birds that have aspired this past 50 million years to live like fish. But inevitably, in this world where *Homo sapiens* dominates, they are threatened. We are not merely predators, we are also ridiculously careless, killing them in their thousands. There is time to stop the rot, though, says Davis. But first we have to care. In brilliant style, *The Plight of the Penguin* shows why we should.

COLIN TUDGE
London, 19 April 2001

Colin Tudge is a science journalist whose abiding interest in the moral philosophy of science is reflected in his widely topical and diverse publications. Some of his publications include *The Engineer in the Garden*, *The Day Before Yesterday*, *Last Animals at the Zoo*, *Neanderthals, Bandits and Farmers*, *The Second Creation: Dolly and the Age of Biological Control* and *The Variety of Life: A Survey and a Celebration of All the Creatures That Have Ever Lived*, which took 10 years to complete. Most recently, he published *In Mendel's Footnotes: Genes and Genetics from the 19th Century to the 22nd.* Currently he is a Research Fellow at the Centre for Philosophy at the London School of Economics.

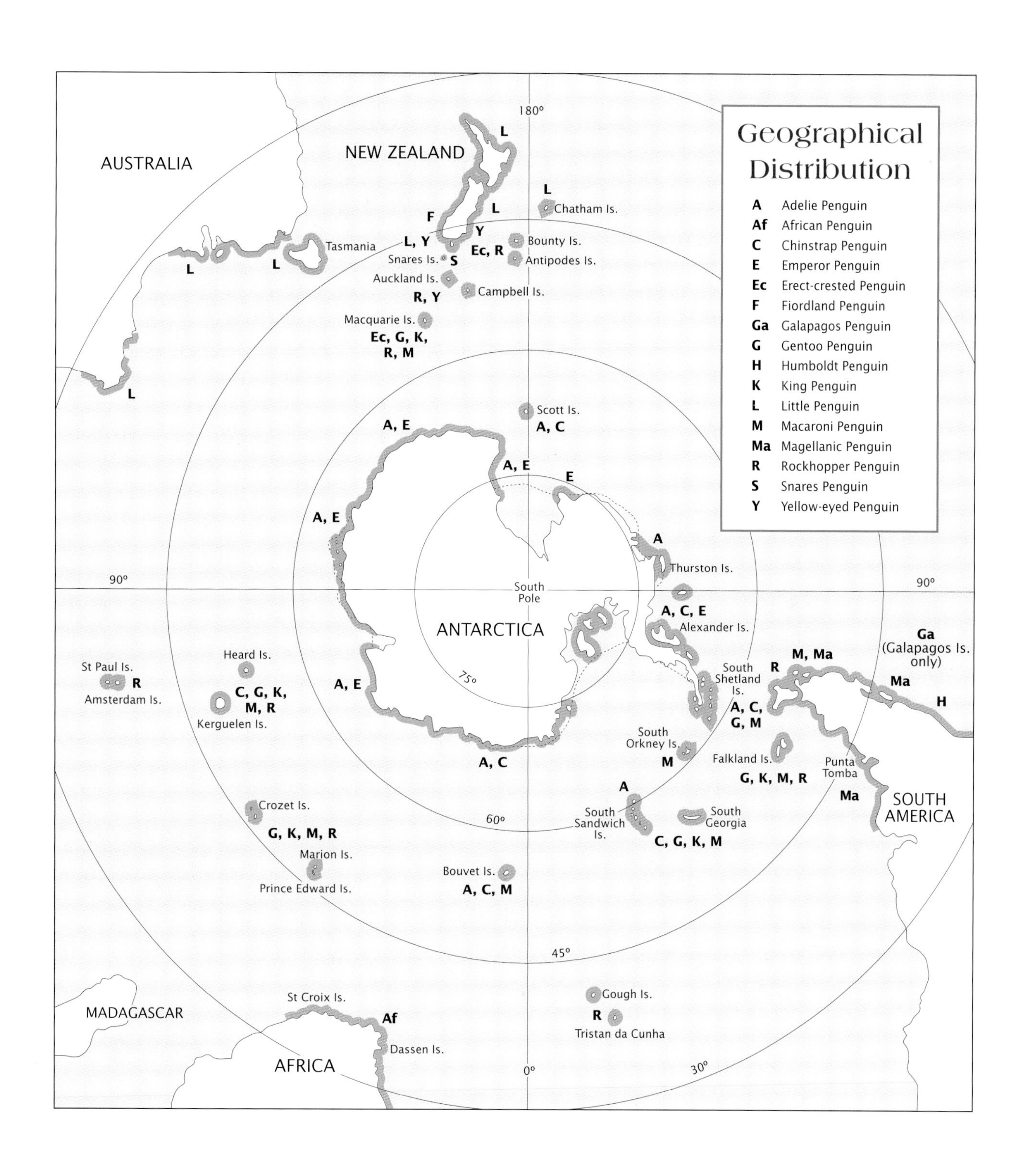
Geographical Distribution
A Adelie Penguin
Af African Penguin
C Chinstrap Penguin
E Emperor Penguin
Ec Erect-crested Penguin
F Fiordland Penguin
Ga Galapagos Penguin
G Gentoo Penguin
H Humboldt Penguin
K King Penguin
L Little Penguin
M Macaroni Penguin
Ma Magellanic Penguin
R Rockhopper Penguin
S Snares Penguin
Y Yellow-eyed Penguin
180°
AUSTRALIA
NEW ZEALAND
Tasmania
Chatham Is.
Bounty Is.
Antipodes Is.
Snares Is.
Auckland Is.
Campbell Is.
Macquarie Is.
Ec, G, K,
R, M
Scott Is.
A, C
South Pole
ANTARCTICA
Thurston Is.
Alexander Is.
South Shetland Is.
South Orkney Is.
Falkland Is.
G, K, M, R
Punta Tomba
SOUTH AMERICA
Ga
(Galapagos Is. only)
South Sandwich Is.
South Georgia
C, G, K, M
Heard Is.
St Paul Is.
Amsterdam Is.
Kerguelen Is.
C, G, K,
M, R
Crozet Is.
G, K, M, R
Marion Is.
Prince Edward Is.
Bouvet Is.
A, C, M
Gough Is.
Tristan da Cunha
St Croix Is.
Dassen Is.
MADAGASCAR
AFRICA
90°
75°
60°
45°
30°
0°

1

History

'History, never repeats

I tell myself before I go to sleep

And there's a light shining in the dark

Leading me on towards a change of heart'

History

Split Enz

What is a penguin?

Birds that want to be fish.

(Photo: Lloyd Spencer Davis)

The answer is not as obvious as you might think. A penguin is, first and foremost, a bird. However, surveys reveal that many people believe that penguins are fish or, even, mammals like us. Their responses illustrate just how hard it is to pigeon-hole penguins. It's like trying to fit a square bird into a round hole – a hole normally occupied by fish.

In a way, that is not an altogether inappropriate view of penguins: birds that want to be fish. Penguins are birds, from the depths of their air sacs to the tips of their feathers, but they are birds that appear to have turned back the evolutionary clock and become like their fishy ancestors again. It would be a mistake, however, to look upon them as half bird, half fish. Rather, they are 100 percent birds disguised somewhat as fish.

8 Popular Misconceptions About Penguins

1 Penguins are a type of fish or mammal

Penguins are birds. They have feathers and lay eggs that must be incubated: defining characteristics of birds. Fossil and genetic evidence shows clearly that penguins are descended from flying birds.

2 Penguins live with polar bears

Although cartoonists persist in showing us this, in fact polar bears are only found in the Northern Hemisphere and penguins only in the Southern Hemisphere.

3 Penguins can survive in water because of a layer of fat

While penguins do have some fat, it is limited both in its depth and effect. Most of the insulation is provided by their feathers, which lock together trapping a layer of air beneath.

4 Penguins are creatures of the snow and ice

The feather survival suits of penguins that enable them to endure long periods immersed in water, permit them to breed in cold places that other birds could only contemplate in their worst nightmares. But penguins are also found breeding on the equator and on the edge of deserts.

5 Penguins are closely related to auks

The Alcidae (auks, auklets and murres) are often cited as the Northern Hemisphere's ecological equivalents of penguins. Indeed, penguins are actually named after the extinct and flightless great auk, whose scientific name is *Pinguinus impennis.* Any resemblance between auks and penguins is, however, only skin deep. It is the result of 'convergent evolution' whereby Natural Selection ends up producing similar forms in unrelated animals that live in similar environments and have similar lifestyles.

6 Penguins mate for life

This is something said of nearly all monogamous colonial seabirds. However, up to 50 percent or more of pairbonds may be broken each year, even when both members of a pair survive from the previous breeding season. Divorce rates can vary widely from species to species and, even, location to location.

7 When penguin chicks form crèches, adults protect and feed each other's chicks

The chicks of several species of penguin congregate together in crèches when the chicks are about two to three weeks old and both parents must go to sea simultaneously to find food for them. While the mere presence of other adults may deter predators like skuas, they don't go out of their way to protect the chicks, which are fed by only their own parents.

8 Penguins push one of their number in to test whether the water is safe from leopard seals

To the casual observer it might look that way. Penguins congregate on the edge of the ice or shore. Despite remarkable adaptations for an aquatic existence, they exhibit a definite reluctance to dive right in. Often their evident fear is a response to the possible presence of leopard seals. However, they simply do not commit ritual sacrifices. Penguins jostle and call while they wait. Eventually one or two may dive in and those behind may hang back, or follow en masse like a black and white waterfall.

This is not as extraordinary as it might seem at first. The sea offers more resistance to movement than does air. For an animal to move quickly and efficiently through water, a streamlined shape is essential. Animals derive their shape and other elements of their design through a process known as Natural Selection. In the sea, those animals with streamlined body designs swim fastest, survive best and go on to reproduce the most. Look anywhere in open water and you will see the same spindle shape repeated again and again, from albacore tuna to great white sharks. You will see it too in turtles, seals, whales and dolphins: animals that, like penguins, returned to the sea after a period of their history was spent on land. Such conformity is what happens when physics meets biology. The physics of moving through water imposes design constraints on all aquatic animals.

Magellanic penguins surfing the waves.
(Photo: Lloyd Spencer Davis)

Penguins, then, have not reversed evolutionary history and become fish again. They have merely become prisoners of the same physical laws that have shaped the body design of nearly all waterborne creatures.

Birds: not in a class of their own

Suppose you took all your clothes and threw them on your bedroom floor. Not only would you then have a room that resembled my son's, you would be faced with one big mess. If we stand back and look at the natural world, it too looks like a mess, with a complex mix of plants and animals spread across the surface of the Earth. One way humans make sense of complexity is to order it. As I keep telling my son: in a normal person's bedroom all the socks go together.

In the eighteenth century, the Swedish naturalist Carl von Linné, better known as Carolus Linnaeus, did for nature what my son cannot do for his apparel. Linnaeus developed a system for ordering plants and animals into hierarchical categories. Each was given a unique two-part name. For example, the domestic dog is *Canis familiaris*. The first part identifies the genus and the second part identifies the species.[1] All similar species are grouped into the same genus, like putting all the socks together. Hence, all dog-like species – wolves, coyotes, jackals – are grouped together in the genus *Canis* and share that generic name. Wolves are *Canis lupus*. Coyotes, *Canis latrans*.

While the members of the genus *Canis* have a lot in common, they also share some things with certain other groups of animals – such as cats, bears and ferrets – and together they make up a more inclusive grouping known as the carnivores. And wouldn't you know it, the carnivores share a few things in common with some other groups, forming the larger grouping that we call mammals. And so on. It's like asking where you live: you could reply with your street address, or the suburb you live in, or the city, the state, the country or the continent. As you move up the hierarchy, each grouping becomes more inclusive, an identity you share with more and more individuals.

[1] Scientific convention means that the genus is always capitalised and the specific name is not, and both are either underlined or italicised.

A marine iguana and Erect-crested penguin are part of the same extended family. *(Photos: Lloyd Spencer Davis)*

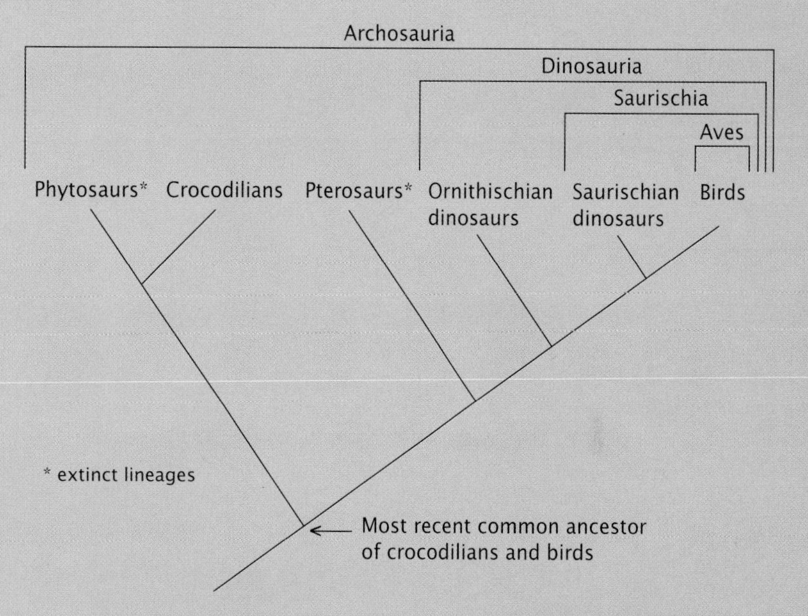

(A) A Cladogram showing the relationships of the Archosauria, the evolutionary lineage that includes living crocodilians and birds.

(B) Cladistic Taxonomy

Archosauria (= crocodilians + dinosaurs + birds + other groups)
  Dinosauria (= dinosaurs + birds)
    Aves (= birds)

(C) Linnean Taxonomy

Class Reptilia (= crocodilians + dinosaurs + other groups)
  Order Crocodilia (= crocodilians)
  Order Dinosauria (= dinosaurs)
Class Aves (= birds)

It is a fine system for grouping information and it would work wonders in a bedroom. The problem for biology is that someone must decide what constitutes a grouping and how it relates to other groups (i.e. is the group the equivalent of a 'city', say, or a 'country'?). That's no big deal if all you want is a system that orders your clothes: who cares whether your jackets go next to your pyjamas or your underpants – either way will do. But implicit in the Linnean system of naming is the assumption that, as well as grouping similar things, it tells you about their evolutionary relationships. And that's the problem. Assign a group to the wrong level in the hierarchy and it can give a completely different message about evolutionary pathways. Now I bet that few amongst us could give a rat's arse whether or not our jeans are ultimately derived from the baggy trousers worn during the French Revolution – we're just happy not to be still prancing about in knee breeches and tights. But as the great geneticist, Theodore Dobzhanksy, so eloquently put it, 'Nothing in biology makes sense except in light of evolution'. For biology, the accuracy of evolutionary relationships is everything.

Under the Linnean system, birds are accorded a level in the classification hierarchy called a Class. This would make them the equivalents of those other classes of terrestrial vertebrates: the amphibians, reptiles and mammals. However, a new system of ordering biological groups, known as cladistics, defines evolutionary relationships more objectively. Using cladistics, birds belong in a grouping with the dinosaurs, making them a sub-group of the reptiles.[2] Birds, it seems, are not the feathered equals of amphibians, reptiles or mammals: in an evolutionary sense they are deserving of a status no more distinct than are crocodiles. Personally, I don't care as long as they keep their rooms tidy.

[2] Using cladistics, or Phylogenetic Systematics as it is sometimes called, some of the naming conventions are different to those of traditional systematics. The grouping that made up reptiles is called Sauropsida, and the mammals, Synapsida.

What is a Bird?

Birds are, in a very real sense, modern dinosaurs. There were essentially two groups of dinosaurs, each with a name that only a palaeontologist could love: the Ornithischia and the Saurischia. The former included duck-billed dinosaurs, armoured dinosaurs like *Stegosaurus* and many other wonderful creatures which no longer walk this planet. The Saurischians are themselves made up of two sub-groups, the Theropoda and the Sauropodomorpha. The latter are all extinct too. They were four-legged creatures that ate only plants and counted among their number the long-necked *Diplodocus* and other 'classic' large dinosaurs. The Theropods, on the other hand, were for the most part carnivorous bipeds – meaning that they walked on only two legs. Included in this group are *Tyrannosaurus rex* and, surprise, surprise, all living birds.

The oldest known bird, *Archaeopteryx*, lived about 150 million years ago and is revealed to us today in half a dozen fossilised specimens. The character that marks *Archaeopteryx* as a bird – indeed, the defining characteristic of all birds – is that it had feathers. Feathers were important to the evolution and subsequent success of birds for two reasons: they provided insulation, which enabled birds to maintain a constant body temperature, and they provided a highly flexible covering with a large surface to weight ratio, which made flight possible. The fossilised impressions of *Archaeopteryx's* feathers show clearly that they were already modified like those of modern flying birds, with the flight feathers on the wings having asymmetrical 'vanes'. In contrast, the feathers of flightless birds like penguins, which serve mainly for insulation, have symmetrical 'vanes'.

Comparison between flight feathers of ***(A) flying birds*** *(asymmetrical vanes), and* ***(B) flightless birds*** *(symmetrical vanes).*

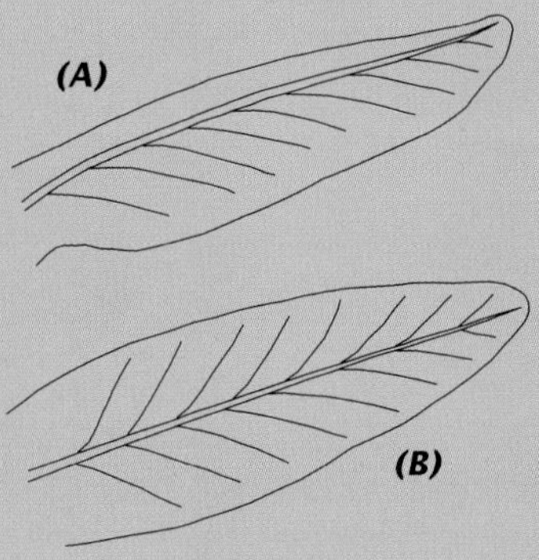

(A)

(B)

Just about all the characteristics of birds are a result of the specialisation required for flight. Their skeletons make use of special struts and airspaces to make them both strong and light. For example, the frigatebird, a distant cousin of penguins, has a two metre wingspan but a skeleton that weighs only 120 grams, which is less than the weight of its feathers. Birds do not have any teeth or heavy musculature associated with chewing (although, interestingly, *Archaeopteryx* still had teeth). They lay eggs, which means that they are not burdened with carrying young, and even their reproductive system remains in a minimal configuration until needed. Only the left oviduct of females is functional and the testes of a male bird can increase 100-fold at the time of reproduction. Thankfully that doesn't happen in humans, otherwise we males would need to push our testicles around in wheelbarrows during the mating season!

Fish do feature on the distant branches of the penguin family tree. About 400 million years ago some lobe-finned fishes tippy-toed on their fleshy pectoral fins up the muddy banks of a Devonian shore. One small step for a lungfish became one giant leap leading to Mankind. From that moment, a whole new world beckoned vertebrates (animals with backbones). They quickly evolved into the many forms we are familiar with today: the amphibians, the reptiles and the mammals. And somewhere along the way, one group evolved certain characteristics such that, forevermore, their descendants would be known as birds.

It is difficult to be precise about just when the first birds that would become penguins walked down to the water's edge, turned their backs on millions of years of this land-based evolution, and dived in. Contrary to early beliefs, penguins are not the remnants of an ancient line of birds that evolved before flight. It is now well established that they are descended from flying birds and evolved much more recently. The earliest verified penguin fossils date back only about 40 million years – over 100 million years after birds began notching up their first flight logs. Older bones, unearthed from

GEOLOGICAL TIME SCALE

Years (millions)	Era	Period	Epoch	
0	CENOZOIC	Quaternary	HOLOCENE	
			PLEISTOCENE	First humans
		Tertiary	PLIOCENE	Human-like ancestors
			MIOCENE	
50			OLIGOCENE	First penguins
			EOCENE	Penguin-like ancestors
			PALEOCENE	First placental mammals
100	MESOZOIC	Cretaceous		
150		Jurassic		First birds First mammals
200		Triassic		First dinosaurs
250	PALEOZOIC	Permian		
300		Carboniferous		First reptiles
350		Devonian		First amphibians
400		Silurian		First jawed fish
450		Ordovician		First vertebrates
500		Cambrian		Origin of many vertebrate groups
550				
600		Precambrian		Algae, sponges

Waipara, New Zealand, show a mixture of penguin characteristics and those of flying birds. They are about 50-60 million years old, from a time geologists refer to as the late Paleocene/early Eocene. It was a time when the Earth was much warmer than it is now. The dinosaurs were already dead. The seals and whales had yet to take the plunge and leave behind their bear- and elephant-like ancestors. In the sea, then, a vast store of riches awaited any bird that could turn back history and become like a fish again.

Except that history never repeats. You can lead a bird to water but you cannot make it sink. The air sacs and hollow bones so necessary for flying birds mean that their specific gravity is lighter than water and, unlike fish, they float. If they were to exploit the wealth of food below the sea's surface, this was just one of the legacies of their flying past that these prototype penguins would have to overcome. They could never truly become fish again. They could never throw off the shackles of being a bird. Forevermore, they would be destined to be phylogenetic[3] cross-dressers and lead lives of compromise.

[3] Phylogeny depicts the relationships between groups of organisms in terms of their evolutionary history.

Turning its back on history: a Snares penguin. (Photo: M Renner)

Humboldt penguins caught at the intersection between two worlds.
(Photo: Lloyd Spencer Davis)

Loony or Goony?

The first penguin fossil was found in New Zealand in 1858, the same year that Charles Darwin presented his controversial theory to the Linnean Society proclaiming that animals were not created but evolved from one another through a process known as Natural Selection. The single fossil bone was sent to London, where Darwin's most ardent supporter, Thomas Henry Huxley, immediately recognised it as a penguin bone but one which was different from any living species. He christened it: *Palaeeudyptes antarcticus*. *Palaeeudyptes* means 'ancient diver' and is an accurate description of the bird to which the bone had belonged. *Antarcticus* is a much less appropriate moniker because New Zealand is actually farther from the Antarctic than London is from the Arctic – but poor ol' Thomas was not to know that.

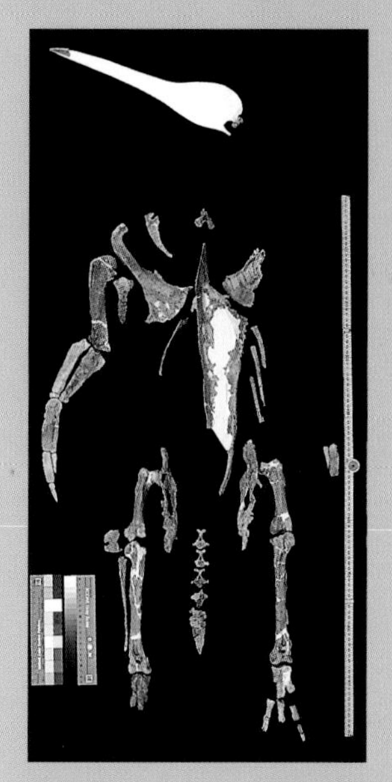

The fossilised bones of Platydyptes, an early penguin from 24 million years ago. *(Photo: E Fordyce)*

Since then, penguin fossils have been found in areas of the Southern Hemisphere that mirror the present-day distribution of penguins: New Zealand, Australia, South America, South Africa, the sub-Antarctic islands and islands off the Antarctic Peninsula. It is apparent from these fossils that, first of all, there were many more different types of penguin in the past than today and, secondly, that the ancestors of penguins must have been flyers. But just which group of flying birds are penguins descended from? That's a question for which nobody has a clear answer.

Comparing their bones, penguins would seem to be most similar to loons (known as 'divers' in Europe) and the group of birds made up of petrels and albatross (which includes the goony bird). Modern techniques, which examine the genetic sequences of DNA contained in the chromosomes (similar to the way DNA fingerprinting is used, for example, to determine the probability that blood found at the scene of a crime came from the accused), also indicate close relationships with loons, petrels and albatross, and frigatebirds. Unfortunately, the resolution of these techniques is insufficient at this stage to be able to identify which one of these candidates is the penguin's closest relative.

Loony or goony? A reconstruction of Platydyptes. *(Illustration: C Gaskin, © E Fordyce)*

Reconstruction of penguin fossils do show a remarkable resemblance to loons. However, we must be wary of superficial similarities: these could arise through convergent evolution as easily as descent from a common ancestor.

2

Aquatic Makeover

'Well, I'm not dumb

but I can't understand

why she walked like a woman

and talked like a man

Oh my Lola'

Lola

The Kinks

In many respects the changes a flying bird must undergo to become an underwater swimmer are no less dramatic than those of transsexuals seeking to change their sex. They must fashion a new body plan, but they must do so out of the parts of the old one. The creation of pectoral fins from wings is really little different to a plastic surgeon manufacturing a vagina from a penis. Except that the transformation of 'genera benders' like penguins is performed by Natural Selection.

Makeover artists: Chinstrap penguins.
(Photo: M Renner)

Flightless steamer duck and entourage in the Falkland Islands.

(Photo: Lloyd Spencer Davis)

The loss of flight is the most obvious modification penguins have undergone in their aquatic makeover. While there are isolated examples of flightless waterbirds – e.g. the flightless steamer duck of the Falklands or the flightless cormorant of the Galapagos – penguins constitute the only group of waterbirds in which every member is flightless. The steamer ducks and Galapagos cormorants evolved on isolated islands without predators and with an abundant supply of food close inshore. Propulsion in water is provided by their large webbed feet and, with little need for flight, there is no advantage to wasting energy on wings. Their wings are now but tiny vestiges of their former glory. In all other respects, however, they are still very much like other ducks or other cormorants. In contrast, the change of lifestyle from bird to fish required a total body makeover for penguins. You don't become a lean mean hunting machine of the high seas with just the equivalent of a nose job.

The problem faced by flying birds is not that they cannot

dive underwater but that there is a trade-off between flying and diving performance. To fly, birds must have relatively light bodies, which means that when they try to dive they use up considerable energy just counteracting the buoyancy of their bodies in water. On the other side of the ledger, the time and depth to which a bird can travel underwater is related to its size. Larger birds can stay down longer and go deeper. But for really large-bodied birds to be able to also maintain the ability to fly, they would need massive wings.[4] Therein lies the rub: to fly you need to be light and have flexible wings with a large surface area to provide lift, while to dive efficiently you need to be large, heavy and have stiff, short and powerful wings.

There comes a certain point, then, when the size of the wings needed to keep a bird aloft is incompatible with underwater swimming. That threshold occurs at about one kilogram. Auks are flyers but, like penguins, rely on diving for their food. Large auks – like puffins – that are near this one kilogram threshold must have relatively short and stubby wings to be able to dive effectively and, as a consequence, are poor flyers. They expend more energy to fly than do

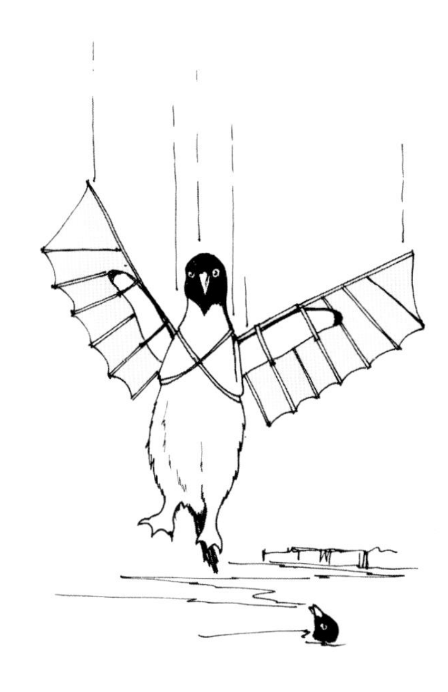

[4] Wing loadings are a measure of the body mass of a bird relative to the surface area of its wings. The smaller the mass in relation to the surface area, the greater the lift that can be generated by the wing. The catch is that as the size of a bird is scaled upwards, the amount of surface area does not increase as fast as the mass (proportional to volume). Hence, to generate the same lift, wings would need to be relatively larger in a big bird than a small bird. Although not birds, pterosaurs were subject to the same laws of gravity: a 17 kilogram *Pteranodon* needed an eight metre wing span to stay aloft!

The king of wings: a Wandering albatross.
(Photo: Lloyd Spencer Davis)

smaller auks like rhinoceros auklets. This limits the flying range of puffins, meaning that they can only breed in places close to their food supply. To increase body size further, while still trying to maintain an ability to fly, would surely negate any advantages of better diving abilities that larger size may bring. Indeed, some extinct auks, such as the great auk, did exceed the one kilogram threshold and all were flightless.

Logically, then, as selection kept pushing the size of divers upwards – there being advantages for birds that could dive deeper and for longer – the transition from flighted to flightless would probably have taken place in birds around the one kilogram threshold. That is, the earliest non-flying penguins would probably have been about one kilogram. As it happens, that is approximately the size of the smallest fossil penguins ever found and is also the size of the smallest living penguin, the Little penguin. Of course, once penguins became flightless, they no longer needed to remain light and were free to rapidly evolve into much larger sizes. The largest penguins, the extinct *Anthropornis nordenskjoeldi*, were up to 1.7 metres tall and tipped the scales at well over 100 kilograms. And you know where a 100 kilogram penguin feeds? Pretty much anywhere it wants!

The world's smallest penguin: the Little penguin.

(Photo: M Renner)

While their new-found aquatic freedom gave these first penguins access to a veritable smorgasbord of new food, underwater life was no picnic. Water conducts heat away from the body more than 20 times faster than does air. That's not a problem for fish, which are cold-blooded. But birds, like us, are warm-blooded. They must maintain a constant body temperature of around 39°C. While this has huge advantages

Convergent Evolution: putting the auk into awkward

Auks are the Northern Hemisphere's equivalents of penguins. *(Photo: M Massaro)*

You could be forgiven for looking at a colony of murres (*Uria lomvia*) and mistaking them for penguins. They look like penguins. They act like penguins. But really any resemblance is only skin deep. Murres are members of a family of birds known as the Alcidae: a group that includes the auks and auklets. The superficial similarity to penguins was not lost on the European mariners who discovered penguins on their forays into the southern seas: they named them after the great auk (*Pinguinus impennis*) – a flightless alcid that was popularly known as a 'penguin' until the last two individuals were shot on 4 June 1844.

Auks are only distantly related to penguins: they are actually descended from gull-like ancestors. It is their similarity of lifestyles not their similarity of genes that produces the resemblance. Just as penguins are only found in the Southern Hemisphere, alcids are only found in the Northern Hemisphere. But within their respective parts of the world, the two groups occupy what ecologists call the same ecological niche. That is, they live in roughly equivalent environments and have an equivalent lifestyle. As Natural Selection will tend to produce forms best adapted for a particular way of living, over evolutionary time two groups occupying similar ecological niches may come to assume the same form. This process is known as convergent evolution. Convergent evolution occurred in Australia where marsupials evolved in the absence of other mammals (placental mammals). Marsupials that engaged in lifestyles similar to those of placental mammals elsewhere evolved similar characteristics, e.g. the recently extinct Thylacine from Tasmania superficially resembled a wolf.

Penguins and auks are both underwater pursuit divers, feeding on similar prey. Given the laws of physics and the constraints associated with swimming underwater, it seems only reasonable that what makes a good design in the Southern Hemisphere should also be a good design in the Northern Hemisphere. The difference is that the potential breeding areas for seabirds in the Northern Hemisphere are all exposed to predators, which means that they cannot afford to give up their ability to fly. As flight seems to be incompatible with pursuit divers over the one kilogram threshold, this has limited the size of the auks (murres are the largest living alcids at 0.95 kilograms). There have been large flightless auks – the great auk and the Californian Lucas auks (*Mancalla* spp.) of the Miocene – but they have all paid the ultimate price for their awkwardness on land and are now long gone.

for flying,[5] animals that must maintain a constant temperature cannot afford to let it drop by more than a few degrees. Just as we would die of hypothermia if left in water too long, so too would penguins if they did not have some form of insulation.

Warm-blooded mammals like whales and seals that, like penguins, followed a yearning to go to sea, insulated themselves with deep layers of blubber.[6] But birds are at a disadvantage here: to comply with the restrictive baggage allowances permissible for flight, birds have been genetically programmed not to accumulate fat in large quantities. While penguins do put down a layer of fat to the extent that they can, it is nowhere near thick enough to permit them to stay at sea for weeks, days, or even, hours on end. To protect themselves from the heat-stealing waters, penguins have had to concoct a survival suit out of the very things that define them as birds: their feathers.

Penguin feathers are short, stiff and hooked, enabling them to lock together, trapping a layer of air between the skin and the feathers. In essence, they act like double-glazing, providing a waterproof insulating layer. In case the penguins should get too hot when on land, the base of the feathers

'Sorry...you're way over the limit.'

[5] A high body temperature means that chemical reactions are much faster – for every ten degrees Celsius rise in temperature, the rate of chemical reactions doubles – permitting rapid conversion of food into the high octane energy necessary to sustain flight.

[6] The pelt of seals also provides some insulation.

even have erector muscles, which enable the penguins to raise their feathers, much like opening louvre windows, to let air circulate between the feathers and the skin.

There is a downside to all this brilliant design: feathers wear out. Feathers are really nothing more than non-living products of the epidermis, much like fingernails or hair. While preening can restore their state to some extent, to maintain them in working order long-term, they must be periodically replaced. And that's a bummer from the penguins' perspective: while they are changing their attire they are, how shall we put it, somewhat exposed. Even though – unlike other

A Rockhopper penguin preens the feathers of its mate.
(Photo: Lloyd Spencer Davis)

birds – the old feathers of moulting penguins do not fall out until the new ones have partially grown underneath, without the full strength of their insulation they must remain on land. Which means going on a crash diet[7] at the very time when they need heaps of energy to manufacture their new suit of feathers. This is where the layer of fat comes in: it is important not so much for insulation as it is to sustain them through long periods when they cannot eat, such as when forced to remain on land for moulting or breeding.

Penguins, having begun the process of phylogenetic surgery, were not about to stop there. In some ways birds are perfect candidates for returning to the water because streamlining is as important for flight as it is for underwater swimming. Even so, the plane-like designs of flying birds are not quite up to it in water. A flying bird must, as well as reducing drag, maintain lift. This means having aerofoils (wings) with a large flattened surface area. In contrast, the density of water keeps animals buoyant so that generating lift to counteract the effects of gravity is not so important for aquatic creatures. On the other flipper, this same density provides much more resistance to a body being propelled through it, accentuating

[7] Penguins need to go to sea to feed.

the amount of drag. Designs that minimize the effort needed to push through water will have an advantage and one design has been proven, time and again, to produce the least drag. A spindle is a cylindrical shape with pointed ends and Natural Selection has repeatedly reproduced this design in all manner of underwater creatures as they have evolved. But there are spindles and then there are penguins. Tests in water tunnels reveal that penguin bodies produce less drag than any boat, car, submarine or aeroplane that scientists and engineers have been able to design.

A spindle shape is common to many animals that must propel themselves through water.

It's not just in their shape that penguins resemble fish. Have a look at their paint job. Take any fish of the open seas – a shark, say – and look at its colour patterning. There are no trees to hide behind in the open ocean, no burrows to sneak into, no long grasses in which to stalk your prey. For this reason, the creatures of the open water, the hunted and the hunter alike, use colour as camouflage. A dark back blends with the murky depths when seen from above, while light bellies are harder to distinguish from the bright surface when looking from below. Sure penguins differ a little – the odd line on their chests, a splash of colour on the cheeks, eyebrows to rival the Russian Politburo – but for the most part they come out of the same school of painting as any mackerel, mako or killer whale.

Spot the odd one out: (from left to right) a Royal sub-species of the Macaroni, an Erect-crested, Leonid Brezhnev, a Gentoo. *(Photos: J Darby, Lloyd Spencer Davis, M Renner; Brezhnev cartoon: I McGee)*

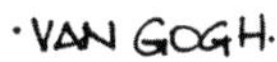

Penguin schools of painting that never really took off.

So if they are just fish in drag, why do we love them so? Penguins appeal universally to humans, even in places where penguins do not live, such as the Northern Hemisphere. A Swedish woman was so besotted with penguins that she carried a stuffed Adelie penguin when she got married instead of a bouquet of flowers.[8] It is much harder to picture a bride walking up the aisle with a wet tuna clutched to her bosom.

Penguins appeal to us because they walk upright like us. We relate to them because they are like us, only with a better dress sense: they appear to wear tuxedoes to work, to play and to sleep in.

The reason penguins walk upright is because they have such damn short legs that are pushed back towards what boaties would call the aft-end of the bird. This is to reduce drag when in the water. The feet provide no propulsion. They are tucked away at the back of the penguin and, with the tail, act like a rudder to help steer the bird.

Birds have a complex foot bone that sounds like it was named by an anatomist with a stutter: it's called a tarsometatarsus. Actually it results from a fusion of some of the bones that in us make up the anklebones (tarsals) and

[8] I know this story to be true: Bengt and Titti were a couple of Swedish hitchhikers I invited to stay while they were honeymooning in New Zealand so that Titti could see her first real penguins.

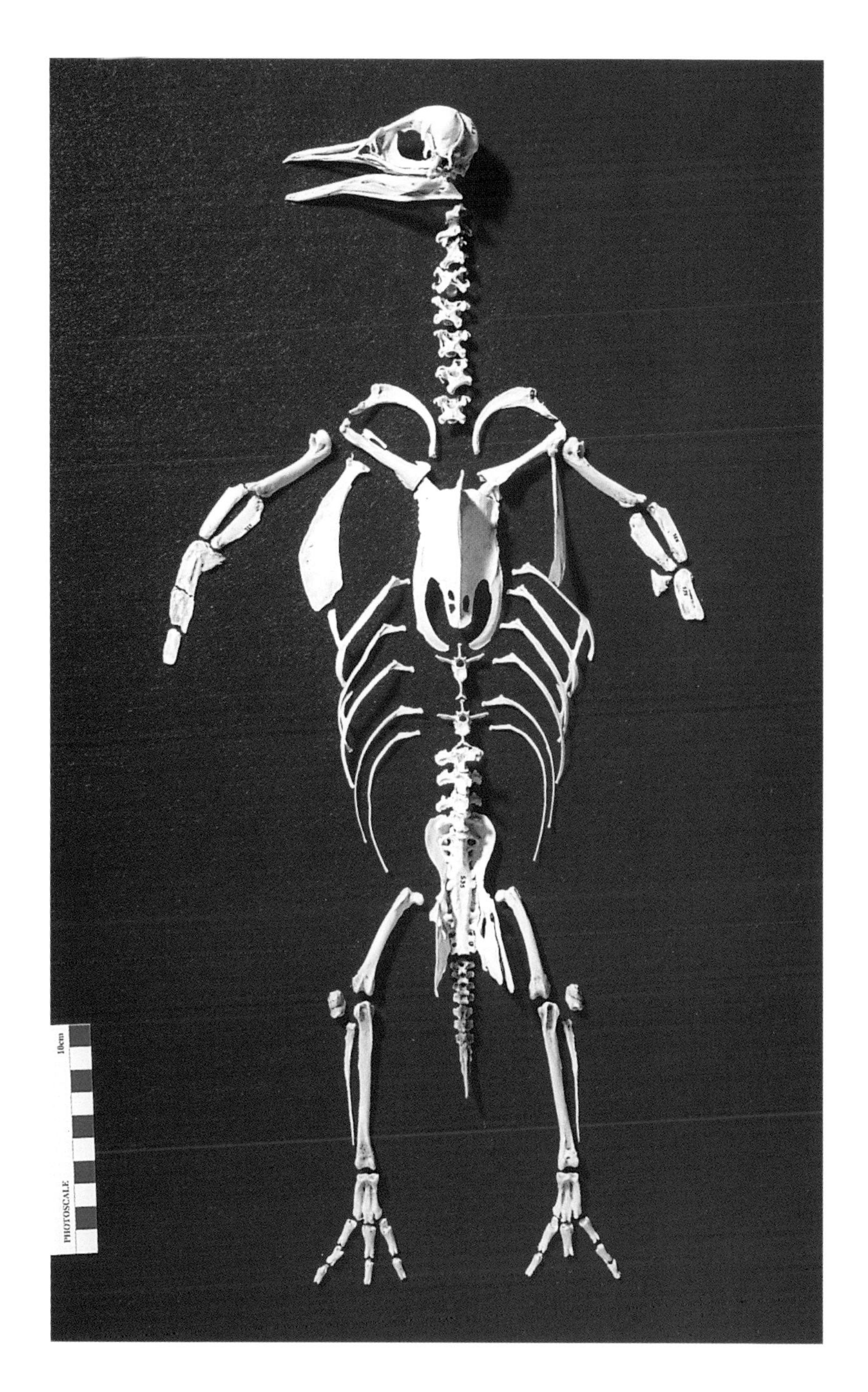

The skeleton of a Little penguin: the tarsometatarsus is the short, wide bone joined to the toes.
(Photo: E Fordyce)

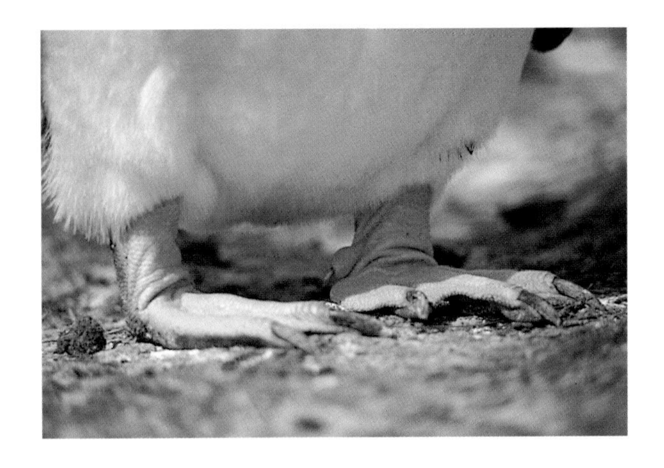

The tarsometatarsus joins the webbed toes of a Gentoo penguin's feet, giving the legs a stubby appearance.
(Photo: Lloyd Spencer Davis)

the arches of our feet (metatarsals). In all birds except penguins, the tarsometatarsus is long and slender. In penguins it is short and wide, contributing to their short legs, upright stance and distinctive waddle. This single bone is so characteristic of penguins that it can be used to irrefutably identify a fossil bone as a penguin: which is just as well, because often palaeontologists have little else to go on.

One of the most dramatic changes to the bones of penguins is not visible from the outside. Flying birds have hollow bones with air spaces to make them light (pneumatic bones). But being light for a diving bird is a distinct disadvantage. The bones of penguins are solid, or non-pneumatic. Compare, say, an Adelie penguin with a similar-sized bird like a common loon. The loon weighs 2.5 kilograms, the penguin 5 kilograms. The difference is air.

While the demands of living in the sea have made penguins conform to a particular pattern, paradoxically this has allowed them to exploit a whole range of different environments on land. The insulation that allows them to endure long hours in cold water pre-adapts penguins to go where others fear to tread: the heart of the Antarctic winter in temperatures that can drop to below minus 60°C. They can also be found breeding on the edge of cactus-covered deserts in Peru and Chile where temperatures can exceed 40°C. This makes them the world's only 100 degree birds. If it is the sea that makes penguins similar, it is the land that gives them their character.

As far as possible, Natural Selection has reconfigured penguins as fish. But like Lola's deep voice, the telltale signs of the original remain. Penguins can never be truly fish-like because, as birds, they lay eggs that must be incubated and, therefore, they have to come ashore to breed.

They must come ashore to breed: Magellanic penguins negotiate elephant seals en route to their colony, Sealion Island, The Falklands.

(Photo: Lloyd Spencer Davis)

Adelie penguins nesting in the midst of an Antarctic storm.

(Photo: Lloyd Spencer Davis)

Humboldt penguins nesting on the edge of a Chilean desert seek shelter from the sun in a cave.

(Photo: Lloyd Spencer Davis)

Penguin Family Album

Lloyd Spencer Davis

Name: Galapagos penguin
Scientific name: *Spheniscus mendiculus*
Distribution: Galapagos Islands
Size: 2.1 kg (male), 1.7 kg (female)
Favourite food: small fish
Nest type: burrow or crevices in lava
Distinguishing characteristics: breeds on the equator, breeds all-year round, probably world's rarest penguin, small bare patch of skin around base of bill

Lloyd Spencer Davis

Name: Magellanic penguin
Scientific name: *Spheniscus magellanicus*
Distribution: Chile, Argentina and the Falkland Islands
Size: 4.9 kg (m), 4.6 kg (f)
Favourite food: small fish
Nest type: burrow or under bushes
Distinguishing characteristics: donkey-like braying call, double black bands across chest, bare patch of skin around base of bill

Lloyd Spencer Davis

Name: Humboldt penguin
Scientific name: *Spheniscus humboldti*
Distribution: Peru and Chile
Size: 4.9 kg (m), 4.5 kg (f)
Favourite food: small fish
Nest type: burrow or cave
Distinguishing characteristics: bare patch of skin around base of bill, single band across chest

Y van Heezik & P Seddon

Name: African penguin
Scientific name: *Spheniscus demersus*
Distribution: southern Africa
Size: 3.3 kg (m), 3.0 kg (f)
Favourite food: small fish
Nest type: burrow or under bushes/rocks
Distinguishing characteristics: donkey-like braying call, single narrow band across chest, bare patch of skin around base of bill

M Renner

Name: Little penguin
Scientific name: *Eudyptula minor*
Distribution: Australia and New Zealand
Size: 1.2 kg (m), 1.0 kg (f)
Favourite food: small fish
Nest type: burrow, cave or under bushes
Distinguishing characteristics:
world's smallest penguin, nocturnal, blue coloration

Name: Yellow-eyed penguin
Scientific name: *Megadyptes antipodes*
Distribution: New Zealand, Auckland Islands, Campbell Island
Size: 5.7 kg (m), 5.4 kg (f)
Favourite food: fish and squid
Nest type: under dense vegetation
Distinguishing characteristics: yellow eyes, yellow band from eyes encircling crown

J Darby

M Renner

Name: Snares penguin
Scientific name: *Eudyptes robustus*
Distribution: Snares Islands
Size: 3.3 kg (m), 2.8 kg (f)
Favourite food: krill, squid and fish
Nest type: in colonies in the open or under forest canopy
Distinguishing characteristics:
yellow crest, appears to have a white 'lip' around bottom mandible

Name: Fiordland penguin
Scientific name: *Eudyptes pachyrhynchus*
Distribution: New Zealand
Size: 4.1 kg (m), 3.7 kg (f)
Favourite food: fish and squid
Nest type: in forest under vegetation or rocks; in caves
Distinguishing characteristics: yellow crest, white stripes on cheeks visible when alert; winter breeder

Lloyd Spencer Davis

Lloyd Spencer Davis

Name: Erect-crested penguin
Scientific name: *Eudyptes sclateri*
Distribution: Antipodes and Bounty Islands
Size: 5.2 kg (m), 5.1 kg (f)
Favourite food: krill and squid
Nest type: in colonies in the open; nest on rocks with little to no nesting material to line nests
Distinguishing characteristics:
yellow upright crest, extreme egg-size differences

Lloyd Spencer Davis

Name: Rockhopper penguin
Scientific name: *Eudyptes chrysocome*
Distribution: circumpolar, sub-Antarctic Islands
Size: 2.5 kg (m), 2.4 kg (f)
Favourite food: krill, fish and squid
Nest type: in colonies in the open; sometimes in association with other species
Distinguishing characteristics:
smallish penguin, crest with long plumes, red eyes

Name: Macaroni/Royal penguin [8]
Scientific name: *Eudyptes chrysolophus*
Distribution: circumpolar, sub-Antarctic Islands
Size: 5.2 kg (m), 5.3 kg (f)
Favourite food: krill
Nest type: in colonies in the open
Distinguishing characteristics:
golden-yellow plumes, drooping behind eye, extreme egg-size differences

C Bradshaw

[8] A sub-species of the Macaroni penguin, the Royal penguin, is a pale-faced variant that breeds only on Macquarie Island. Often listed by authorities as a separate species *Eudyptes schlegeli*.

Name: Gentoo penguin
Scientific name: *Pygoscelis papua*
Distribution: circumpolar, sub-Antarctic Islands and Antarctic Peninsula
Size: 5.6 kg (m), 5.1 kg (f)
Favourite food: krill and fish
Nest type: in colonies in the open
Distinguishing characteristics:
white patch above each eye, orange-red bill, white eye ring

R Cuthbert

M Renner

Name: Chinstrap penguin
Scientific name: *Pygoscelis antarctica*
Distribution: circumpolar, sub-Antarctic Islands and Antarctic Peninsula
Size: 5.0 kg (m), 4.8 kg (f)
Favourite food: krill
Nest type: in colonies in the open
Distinguishing characteristics: white face with thin black line crossing throat under chin

Lloyd Spencer Davis

Name: Adelie penguin
Scientific name: *Pygoscelis adeliae*
Distribution: Antarctic
Size: 5.4 kg (m), 4.7 kg (f)
Favourite food: krill
Nest type: in colonies in the open, use stones to line nest
Distinguishing characteristics: black head, white eye rings

Lloyd Spencer Davis

Name: King penguin
Scientific name: *Aptenodytes patagonicus*
Distribution: sub-Antarctic and Antarctic islands
Size: 16.0 kg (m), 14.3 kg (f)
Favourite food: fish, some squid
Nest type: in colonies in the open, have territories but no nest
Distinguishing characteristics: orange ear patches with orange plate on slender lower bill, single egg

Lloyd Spencer Davis

Name: Emperor penguin
Scientific name: *Aptenodytes forsteri*
Distribution: Antarctic
Size: 36.7 kg (m), 28.4 kg (f)
Favourite food: fish and squid
Nest type: breed on sea ice in winter, egg carried on feet
Distinguishing characteristics: largest penguin, yellow ear patches, pink plate on lower bill, single egg

3

Sex

'Well there's a rose in the fisted glove
and the eagle flies with the dove
and if you can't be with the one you love, Honey
love the one you're with'

Love the One You're With
Crosby, Stills, Nash and Young

Penguins are monogamous, meaning that one male pairs with one female and they work together to raise the offspring. Monogamy sounds a lot like marriage and marriage sounds a lot like us, and that is the basis for one of the most popular misconceptions about penguins. Pick up any magazine article about penguins, watch any natural history documentary about penguins, and likely as not it will tell you that they 'mate for life'. It's as if we have tried to

Erect-crested penguins making out: preening each other (allopreening) is a way some penguins reinforce their pairbond. (Photo: M Renner)

Snares penguins in search of a mate. Which one to choose?

(Photo: M Renner)

impose upon these birds our romantic ideals of marriage without ever realising that penguins are no less prone than we are to relationship break-ups, a quick one on the side, or sexual perversions. When it comes to love, penguins are among the world's greatest pragmatists. If they had an anthem it would have to be 'Love the one you're with'.

The persistence of the till-death-do-us-part scenario is, however, rooted in scientific theory and, as perverse as it may sound, it is because they all look alike.

Cartoonists have made penguins an icon for uniformity, for sameness, for blandness. In one cartoon, two penguins confront each other surrounded by countless others just like them. Says one to the other, 'How the Hell do I know if I'm the same one you mated with last year?' It is vintage cartooning. Yet, all joking aside, the questions it raises are very real ones. How do they tell each other apart? How do they know which one to mate with? And, why do they all look alike?

Look at any congregation of penguins and it is hard not to be struck by the notion that they are somehow clones of each other. It's impossible to tell the Bills from the Jills, let alone the Lolas. To be fair, this uniformity is actually a characteristic of seabirds generally. Look at gannets. Look at albatross. Look at gulls.

Based on our own species, we might expect the sexes to differ at least. Beards and breasts and other sex differences result from a process known as Sexual Selection (see: *Sexual Selection*, p.49). But male and female seabirds are to all intents and purposes identical, or *monomorphic* as the scientists love to say. Therefore, sexual selection in seabirds is presumed to be of little consequence.

Seabirds lay large eggs that have very long incubation periods. Penguin eggs, for instance, must be incubated for over a month. During this period a parent needs to be with the eggs at all times to keep them warm and protect them from predators. Of course, while on land a parent cannot eat. Also, once the chicks hatch, food must be brought to them on a regular basis. All this is too much for one parent to handle so both mum and dad must work together to care for the offspring if they are to have any chance of breeding successfully. If male penguins were to forgo parental duties in favour of searching for other mating opportunities, as many other animals do (see: *Parental Investment*, p.50), their offspring

Sexual Selection

When I was about ten, I got hold of a book with a large pair of breasts on the cover and the rather dubious title, *Confessions of a Window Cleaner*. By today's standards it was about as risqué as *Wind in the Willows* but at the time I thought I had found the Holy Grail of all things forbidden. Consequently, when my mother discovered it, I was mightily embarrassed, to say the least, but not completely without my wits. I told her that I was reading a book about cleaning windows. This from a guy who made his bed once a month – whether it needed it or not.[9]

I must have thought that my mother wasn't born yesterday but well before the last bloody Ice Age. To be honest though, while at the time I knew about this thing called 'sex', it never occurred to me that my parents practised it, least of all, that they might have used it to create me.

My childhood confusion about the consequences of sex is not something peculiar to me. Charles Darwin was one of many scientists and philosophers who have spent a lot of time thinking about sex and the reasons for it – although, to be fair to him, he also had ten children. While Darwin's concept of Natural Selection is often popularised as 'survival of the fittest', he recognised that from an evolutionary point of view it wasn't just survival that mattered, but reproduction also. Individuals with attributes that increased the likelihood that they would have sex – rather than just read about it in third-rate paperbacks – would have more offspring and, therefore, those attributes, which would be inherited by their offspring, would become more apparent in the population.

Darwin termed this process 'Sexual Selection' and he saw it functioning in two ways: through attributes which give members of one sex an edge in competing against each other for members of the opposite sex, or through choice by members of one sex for attributes they find attractive in the other sex. So, for example, the antlers of red deer stags and the large body size of male elephant seals are used to bully other males out of their fornicating way, so to speak. Whereas, females may use the number of 'eyespots' in a peacock's tail or the deepness of a male frog's voice to select which male they'd prefer to do the wild thing with. Darwin saw all this and realised that it would lead to differences between the sexes – sexual dimorphisms – but he had no idea as to why it should mainly be males that were competitive and females that were choosy.

The battle of the bulge: male elephant seals.

(Photo: Lloyd Spencer Davis)

[9] Okay, so maybe it's genetic. I get it from my son.

Parental Investment

For many years it was fashionable amongst population geneticists to conduct mating experiments by putting male fruit flies into milk bottles with groups of virgin female fruit flies. When a British guy called Bateson did this, almost a century after Darwin described sexual selection, he observed that whereas nearly all the females produced offspring, many males produced no offspring at all, while a few did spectacularly well. Furthermore, the number of offspring a female produced did not alter with the number of partners she had, whereas for males, the more female fruit flies they mated with, the greater was the number of baby fruit flies that resembled them.

Bateson's genius lay not in the technical wizardry of his experimental design, but in the brilliance of his insight. He reasoned that the differences we observe in male and female sexual behaviour all come down to differences in the size of the female's eggs and the male's sperm. Eggs are relatively large and costly to produce – what with all the nutrients needed to nourish a developing embryo – and females produce relatively few of them. A human female, for example, would be lucky to produce 300 – 400 viable eggs over her lifetime. In contrast, sperm are tiny, inexpensive, and males produce them by the bucketload. Okay, I exaggerate a little, but a single human male ejaculate may contain 300 – 400 million sperm, enough to fertilise all the females in the United States more than twice over!

And that is the nub of it. Sperm are cheap. Eggs are expensive. Males can afford to sow their wild oats wherever they want, for what does it matter if a few – hell, a few million – fall on barren ground? For females, each egg is much more valuable and its reproductive potential should not be squandered. It is much more important that they concentrate on choosing Mr Right. But the female's burden doesn't stop there.

Because of the size of their investments in mating (sperm vs egg), males will be more inclined to walk away from it. Consider two people making a business venture, one invests $1 and the other $1,000,000: which one has the most to lose if the business fails? Sex is like that. Males can afford to go off to compete with other males for new mating opportunities, but females cannot risk losing their investment. So males are inherently competitive philanderers, leaving females saddled with the primary responsibility for rearing the offspring.

Yellow-eyed penguin with chick.

(Photo: J Darby)

would never survive. To the casual observer, this enforced monogamy seems to give a male penguin little opportunity for being unfaithful, even if he does produce enough sperm to fertilise all the female penguins in Antarctica twice over.

If males get to breed with only one female irrespective of whether they look like a penguin Mr Bean or a movie star, then the penguin equivalents of a strong jawline and perfect hair will be no more likely to be passed on to the next generation than will the equivalents of rubber lips, a funny walk and a penchant for driving minis rather badly. Selection for secondary sexual characteristics of males can occur only when those characteristics allow the males to father more offspring than males not so well endowed. Without any sexual selection, males and females will tend to remain the same. That's the standard scientific explanation anyway – but in penguins it is not that simple.

If sex is the biological rhythm to which we all respond, sometimes it seems that we march to the beat of a distant drummer. There are many obstacles that we must overcome before getting to the finale, and penguins are no exception. And it's not foreplay we're talking about here: this is more like one-, two- and three-play.

A pair of blue-footed boobies in the Galapagos Islands. The male has the smaller pupils.

(Photo: Lloyd Spencer Davis)

The first thing a penguin must do is decide where to breed. It is one thing for a flying seabird like a gannet to select some high clifftop sanctuary free from the scourge of predators, but for a bird that must walk on land – upright and on short little legs at that – the options are more limited. Penguins must find places to breed that are close to the shore. Most breed within spitting distance of the sea.[10]

Yellow-eyed penguins breeding on the Auckland Islands provide a minor exception to this spitting rule: they may walk up to two kilometres inland to nest within forest. A home nestled beneath mature trees, with few neighbours and no sea views is not what we expect to find when scouring the penguin real estate pages. But what makes an appropriate nest site for penguins varies enormously, especially with latitude. The same survival suit of feathers that prevents body heat escaping when in water can become a right liability when on land. This is particularly so in the tropics and temperate regions. In these areas it is important for the birds to have nest sites protected from the sun, otherwise they would quickly overheat. The Galapagos Islands are on the equator and Galapagos penguins find shelter by breeding within the cracks

[10] Not that penguins spit exactly, although they do have extremely large salt glands, which remove the salt from the seawater they swallow. A thick salty liquid continually drips from their nostrils, as if they have a cold, and runs down to the tips of their bills. There it collects and will eventually fall off unless the bird shakes its head, whereupon it flies off in all directions like great gobs of spit.

of old lava flows. Humboldt penguins manage to live on the edge of cactus-studded deserts by nesting in caves or burrows. African, Magellanic and Little penguins are also primarily burrow nesters. In temperate regions like those in southern New Zealand, Yellow-eyed and Fiordland penguins find shelter in forests. Farther south, in the sub-Antarctic and Antarctic, ambient air temperatures are cool enough to permit penguins to breed out in the open.

Desert-living Humboldt penguin.

(Photo: Lloyd Spencer Davis)

Of course, being unable to fly means that penguins must construct their nests on the ground, and that limits the type of nests they can build. To start off with, the eggs need to be kept dry. Burrow and cave-dwellers have an advantage here, as the ground should already be dry and there is little need to do anything other than line the nest with a little grass. In temperate and sub-Antarctic areas, grasses and vegetation are used to build a nest. Antarctic penguins, without vegetation at their disposal, are forced to line their nests with stones and appropriate stones can become a much sought after commodity. Emperor penguins don't actually breed on land at all; they breed on frozen sea-ice and, as such, have nary a plant nor stone at their flipper tips. They get around this dilemma by producing only one large egg that they carry on their feet. Oddly, the closely-related King penguins, which breed in the sub-Antarctic and have their choice of millions of stones or tons of vegetation, do likewise. It might be inferred from this that the ancestors of King penguins were once like Emperor penguins, and that King penguins still carry their eggs as a sort of phylogenetic hangover from an evolutionary party they left a long time ago.

While the best thing about nesting on the ground is that it's not far to fall out of bed, it does have its drawbacks. The penguins and their offspring are potentially vulnerable to predators. Like most flightless birds, it seems certain that penguins could only have evolved in areas where there were few or no predators. One reason why penguins could never co-exist with polar bears is simply that penguins would be sitting ducks (or more accurately, dead ducks). And if the polar bears didn't get them, the wolves or the wolverines would.

The reason auks, the Northern Hemisphere's ecological equivalents of penguins, aren't flightless is simply because they cannot afford to be without their wings.

Penguins evolved in the Southern Hemisphere in places like New Zealand and other islands free of mammalian predators. Ironically another mammal would later transport such predators from the Northern Hemisphere to the Southern Hemisphere, upsetting the natural balance and putting the continued existence of penguins at risk. Now cats stalk penguins on sub-Antarctic islands, foxes scan breeding colonies in Australia, and stoats eye penguin chicks in New Zealand.

A Brown skua attempting to steal an egg from a Rockhopper penguin.

(Photo: Lloyd Spencer Davis)

The threat to penguins does not only come from those on four feet. Other seabirds, especially skuas, sheathbills, giant petrels and gulls have learnt that penguin colonies offer easy pickings (see: *Colonies*, p.57). The best defence penguins have against such killers of their eggs and chicks is to nest together. Birds of a feather flock together for a reason, and it isn't because they like each other. In essence the colony functions like a herd, reducing the risk for any one bird.

Sometimes this can lead to more than one species of penguin nesting together in the same colony. On the Antipodes

Islands, Rockhopper penguins nest within Erect-crested penguin colonies, while on Ardley Island, off the Antarctic Peninsula, Gentoo, Chinstrap and Adelie penguins all nest together. And in the Falkland Islands, Rockhopper penguins will even nest in amongst blue-eyed shags for protection.

Finding a suitable place to breed, however, is just the beginning. Next the hopeful bird must attract a mate. Penguins breed in colonies that can vary from a few couples to a few hundred thousand couples. You'd think that finding a mate in such a marketplace would be easy: but it is not as easy as it sounds.

The Adelie penguin colony at Cape Bird, Ross Island, Antarctica.
(Photo: Lloyd Spencer Davis)

Colonies

It was more-or-less by accident that I came to study penguins. I had been accepted to go to Antarctica to conduct research on Weddell seals but, at the last minute and for reasons that would take too long to explain here, I was required to change topics. I opted to study Adelie penguins instead.

When I arrived at the Cape Bird colony,[11] where more than 60,000 penguins breed, I was instantly smitten by penguins. But one question continues to nag me since that first encounter. Why do they nest in small discrete sub-colonies rather than the large colonies typical of most seabirds? One thing my research showed clearly was that birds that nested on the outside edge of the sub-colonies were only half as likely to successfully rear their young as were birds in central nests. This is because penguin nests on the periphery are exposed to skuas, which can more easily divest them of their eggs and chicks. If the penguins were to form just one large colony, like gannets, say, then a much smaller proportion of them would be exposed to the outside and the skuas.

Penguins breeding in Antarctica do face another danger and that is the potential for snowmelt to flood their nests. Hence, it is argued that they cannot form a single colony because they can only nest along ridges and places likely to be free from the threat of snowmelt. While there is undoubtedly some truth to this, it cannot explain the whole story. Sub-colonies come and go, expand and contract. Very often two sub-colonies will expand and coalesce into one, proving that the intervening ground was suitable for breeding all along. So why not start off with one colony and minimize the number of exposed nests?

Flying birds that are colonial breeders are able to drop down onto their central nests. Penguins, however, must run a gauntlet of pecks from their neighbours as they force their way into a colony from the outside. Some have suggested that this may limit the depth of a colony. But this argument holds even less water than a penguin nest atop a ridge: Macaroni and King penguins manage to have single large colonies consisting of tens if not hundreds of thousands of birds.

At the other end of the spectrum, there are Yellow-eyed penguins. They nest in forest, often hundreds of metres from neighbouring nests. Is it because they find it difficult to find the right combination of foliage that offers protection from the sun? Or perhaps traditionally they did not have any land-based predators and found other advantages from seeking solitude? As Yellow-eyed penguin pairs stay together year-round there is little need for the approach to sex that the colony offers and, perhaps, by being apart, males lessen the risk that they will be cuckolded?

I still don't know the complete answer to why Adelie penguins nest in the groups they do. On the one hand penguins seem to want to be together, on the other, they don't. It is one of the great paradoxes about penguins that they are so unsociably gregarious. They go to great lengths to seek each other out and then behave like selfish little brats.

[11] It used to be common for people to refer to a collection of breeding penguins within a geographic area as a rookery, and the smaller breeding groups that made up the rookery were termed colonies. However, to standardise usage, and to bring it into line with the use of colony in other colonial seabirds, the former is now called a colony and the smaller breeding groups are known as sub-colonies.

Wall-to-wall penguins: a colony of King penguins on Macquarie Island.
(Photo: C Bradshaw)

As with most animals, males can get mates by either competing against other males for access to females or showing off in a way that attracts females. There is evidence that penguins do both. While the males don't fight over females directly (interestingly, the females will fight over males), by competing for nest sites the outcome can be the same. Get a good nest site and a male is likely to get a mate. So penguin punch-ups over parking spaces are not uncommon.

Most penguins do not stay at the breeding grounds all year round. In migratory species, the males typically arrive at the colony a few days before the females and, in some, like the crested penguins and Magellanic penguins, they can arrive up to a couple of weeks earlier. From a penguin's perspective there are three things that make good real estate: location, location, location. The location of a nest, in terms of how well it is protected from predators and the elements, will have a huge bearing on the prospects of eggs laid in it. Good nests are highly desirable, and males with the finest properties seldom need worry about remaining celibate. Just ask any billionaire.

Despite the appearances of no sexual differences, in fact, penguins are subtlely dimorphic: males tend to be slightly bigger than females in body size and bill size. In those migratory species where males must compete for a mate each season, as opposed to species where pairs stay together throughout the year, the degree of that sexual dimorphism is most exaggerated. Curiously, many of those penguins that compete most vigorously for nest sites are fish eaters and have a hook at the end of their bill used to hold onto fish. As many a penguin researcher has learnt, this hook is also an effective weapon, able to slash a foe's face or a penguin researcher's arm in a flash.

Having secured a site, a male will then set about the business of building a nest and advertising for a mate. They don't exactly put an advertisement in the personal columns, but it's close. Typically a male will perform a display on or near his nest site. Like boisterous drunks at a pub, it usually involves a lot of arm waving and calling. This is often socially contagious, inciting an outbreak in the colony of singing males waving their arms about.

It is a clue to how females determine which penguin to

Standing out from the crowd: a rare genetic colour morph of the Adelie penguin at its nest with its normal-coloured partner.
(Photo: Lloyd Spencer Davis)

mate with even though they all look pretty much alike. Each male's call is as individually distinct as a fingerprint. Not only that, the females can use the calls to extract information about the males.

From the female's perspective it is important to choose a male that is likely to be successful. For many penguins that means choosing a male that can withstand the periods of fasting necessary when incubating the eggs. Therefore, for a female penguin, a sexy male is a fat male.

Females exhibit a preference for males with deep voices.

Bigger males have larger chest cavities and, as a consequence, deeper voices. However, while choosing a large male would on average offer some indication of his staying power – because larger males have bigger fuel tanks – what a female really needs is a *big fat* male. Theoretically, at least, it is possible that females can determine how fat a male is from his call too. Calls are produced by the syrinx – the bird equivalent

Gentoo penguins calling to each other. Does the male's call contain information about his potential as a father?
(Photo: M Renner)

of a voicebox – which is located in the upper chest. This is also a significant area for fat storage. The more fat that surrounds the syrinx, the more it should attenuate the call, absorbing the high frequencies and making the call sound flat. Potentially, females may be able to pick their ideal mate by listening for a deep flat call. The beauty of such a system is that, unlike boisterous drunks at a pub, male penguins cannot lie or cheat. They cannot lie about how many resources they have or how big various parts of their anatomy are because the truth determines the form of their calls.

As a consequence of this selection, males have become somewhat larger than females. This size difference is greatest in those species where the male must fast the longest and where it will pay females most to be choosy. Although males and females look ostensibly the same, the subtle differences in body and bill size should alert us to the fact that sexual selection is relevant to penguins.

On the face of it, male penguins might appear to be the original SNAGs (Senistive New Age Guys): devoted to their wives, undertaking more than their share of domestic duties (in many species of penguin, males do most of the incubating) and protecting their young. But really, they are just wolves in SNAG's clothing. Strip off the black and white apron and underneath lie the same primal urges that drive Bateson's fruit flies (see: *Parental Investment*, p.50). Monogamy acts as little more than a handbrake – retarding rather than eliminating the urge to copulate with as many females on the planet as is penguinly possible.

Male penguins, like most males, are none too discriminating. Their idea of a sexual strategy is to set up a nest site and then court any female that comes within earshot of their mating calls. The big problem for males is that there are not enough females to go around, and many find their calls go unanswered.

There are two reasons for this. Firstly, although equal numbers of male and female eggs are laid, females don't live as long as males. Females start breeding at a younger age – and as any parent can tell you, that is bound to take years off your life! This is not only because of the increased exertion needed to fend for the young, but also because a parent must make regular trips to sea to get food to feed its chicks, thereby exposing itself to greater risk of predation. Penguins breeding in

Doing lunch the hard way: with a leopard seal.

(Photo: Lloyd Spencer Davis)

the Antarctic are vulnerable to being killed by leopard seals, particularly at the ice edge as they get into or out of the water. A breeding penguin may have to cross that dangerous margin between land and water up to 40 times more than a non-breeder in a single season, making it much more likely they will become a snack for a leopard seal.

Another reason why there never seems to be enough females is that virtually all the males arrive at the colony ahead of the females – they've got to be there if they are going to have any chance at the only game in town. Because the females don't all arrive at once, a female faces the prospect of being courted by any available unpaired males when she does. This is what biologists call the Operational Sex Ratio – to distinguish it from the actual ratio of males to females in the population – and it is a measure of how many males are physically available to each female at the time she comes to breed.

Males, while they continue to do the penguin equivalent of wolf-whistling at anything that walks, can best maximize their chances of a successful coupling by trying to reunite with their previous season's partner. They do this by returning to their previous nest site, which they use as a meeting point. This is why males are so attached to their nest sites: up to 99 percent of male Adelie penguins may use the exact same piece of ground from one season to the next on which to make their nest.

But it takes two to rendezvous as much as to tango. So what's in it for the females, why do they go back to their old nest site too? When selecting a new mate, females can use clues from the location of his nest or the cut of his call to deduce whether he will make a good partner, but it is an imperfect science. Far better, if having already identified a winner, that you stick with him.

Females that bred successfully in the previous season do just that, tending to stand by their man in contrast to females that were unsuccessful. By returning to the old nest site they are able to meet up with their male, which they identify by the individually distinct characteristics in his call. When reuniting, a pair indulges in something like necking, calling to each other and waving their necks together. If a male and female did not manage to rear offspring successfully the year before, the female is likely to divorce such a poor chap. So much for mating for life – in some species the divorce rate is up to 50 percent; not so different to us humans. And as for Emperor penguins, which do not have nest sites and, therefore, no well-defined rendezvous point, the divorce rate skyrockets even among successful breeders.

An Adelie pair reunites.

(Photo: M Renner)

Another element that also affects the longevity of penguin relationships is the time available for breeding. This is especially so for those penguins that breed at high latitudes (i.e. towards the South Pole) and so have a relatively short summer in which to rear their chicks. They don't have the luxury of waiting for a male, no matter how good a husband he might have been in the past. And so, they opt to love the one they're with. A female Adelie penguin will mate within hours, if not minutes, of arriving at the colony at the start of the breeding season. If her old partner is not there, she will simply bonk one of the nearby males. That way, if her proven but tardy male does eventually show up, she can drop the new model and return to the old. Such pragmatism produces problems of its own. If the original female partner of the new male arrives at the colony to find him otherwise engaged, she is likely to take exception to the new arrangement and drive the usurping female away in a furious flurry of blows from her flippers, setting the whole process off again. Courtship in a penguin colony resembles nothing so much as musical chairs.

The upshot is that there is often a lot of mate swapping going on in a penguin colony. Monogamy to a penguin doesn't mean having just one mate, it means having just one mate at a time. Although even this is not quite true: close inspection of penguin mating behaviour reveals that a few females are not averse to having a quick one on the side with a neighbour even while remaining paired, and some could even be accused of soliciting sex (see: *The Other Side of Penguins: life in the closet*, p.69).

The Other Side of Penguins: life in the closet

Homosexual behaviour is actually quite widespread in the animal kingdom. Male penguins, fired up with testosterone at the start of the courtship period, will try to mount anything vaguely resembling a penguin. Like extras in a Clint Eastwood movie, their *modus operandi* seems to be 'shoot now, ask questions later'. This can sometimes lead to males mounting other males. Given the opportunity, they will even try to copulate with toy penguins. Males of another flightless bird – New Zealand's kakapo, the world's most endangered parrot with only some 60 individuals still alive – have even been known to copulate with a researcher's shirt (and they wonder why they're endangered!). The point is, males can afford to be bad at sex because they are given so many bullets to play with. Taking into account how poor male penguins are at the act itself (see: *Sperm Competition*, p.70), perhaps a little practice can help make perfect, whether it be on each other, a toy or the shirt off your back.

Females, it seems, have long known that they can utilise to their own advantage the fact that males are ruled by their reproductive organs and not their brains. In the case of Adelie penguins, stones are important for lining nests to protect them from meltwater (see: *Colonies*, p.57). As stones are often limited in supply, they become the currency of the colony, often stolen and often fought over. Once the female has laid her eggs, and before she goes off to sea leaving her partner to incubate them, she will typically go in search of stones to shore up their nest. Sometimes this means stealing stones from other nests. But some females have learnt to use sex to dupe unsuspecting males out of the stones they have worked so hard to collect.

The female will approach an unpaired male in a position that suggests that she wants to have sex. The male, excited at the prospect, readily moves aside for the female. However, instead of lying down in the nest to consummate the moment, the female simply takes the money and runs: she helps herself to a stone and scurries back to her own nest. As if to prove just how gullible males can be, it is not uncommon for the female to return and repeat the procedure with the same male up to 20 times.

Given that these males are unpaired, it could be argued that they have little to lose but their dignity and a few stones. And, on a few occasions, females do actually trade sex for a stone. As penguins have been around for 50 million years or so, perhaps it really is the oldest profession in the world?

Takes the money and runs.

(Photo: Lloyd Spencer Davis)

Sperm Competition

Perhaps it is a consequence of their fish-like fancy dress, but male penguins are not good at sex. Like most birds, the male must stand on the female's back, working his way down to her nether regions before bringing their copulatory organs (cloaca) into the briefest of contacts. However, balancing on a female's back becomes much more difficult when having to stand upright on tiny legs, being deprived of the wings that other seabirds use to prop themselves up with by resting the tips upon the ground. Flippers, by comparison, are stubby useless things that male penguins can do little more than wave frantically about in a desperate bid to maintain their balance.

As a result, many males simply fall off the female before getting down to the business end. Even those that manage to, often shoot when unbalanced, firing sperm all over the place. Over the ground. Over the female. Anywhere but into her reproductive tract. Others simply fire blanks: unable to discharge any sperm.

As perverted as it sounds, some people actually watch this sort of thing for a living.[12] What those observations show is that roughly one-third of mating attempts by males fail to deliver, another third miss the target and only about one in three hit the bullseye.

It is only recently that scientists have started to realise that the same process of sexual selection that leads to male-male competition before copulation, can lead to competition among sperm afterwards. Think of it this way. Just as there is selection for attributes like antlers and horns that give males an advantage in getting partners, similarly, if females mate with more than one male, attributes that increase the likelihood of a male's sperm getting to fertilise the eggs will proliferate.

[12] Well, okay, maybe there are only two of us.

Many rodents use copulatory plugs to bung up the female's reproductive tract and prevent the sperm from another male getting in. Some animals produce 'killer sperm' that act like hit men, taking out the sperm from other males. The two most common forms of sperm competition occur through mechanisms which result in either last male sperm precedence (meaning that something tilts the odds in favour of the sperm from the last male that the female mates with) or proportional representation (meaning something is done to increase the proportion of a male's sperm in the female's reproductive tract, thereby increasing his odds of siring the offspring).

For male penguins the stakes are high. The last male that the female pairs with has to invest a great deal in rearing the chicks, and his evolutionary future would look very bleak if he were to waste his energies rearing another male's progeny. Paternity tests using DNA fingerprinting reveal that such situations seldom occur despite the relatively high levels of mate switching. While it is possible that there are some as yet unexplained mechanisms that result in last male sperm precedence, proportionality plays a part. A male swings the odds in his favour by continuing to copulate repeatedly with a female for longer if she had a previous partner than if she had no previous partner. Copulation rates are also higher in those species like Adelies where mate switching is common compared to species like Erect-crested penguins where it is rarer. On the other flipper, when the roles are reversed, males engaging in a quick one on the side actually transfer more sperm than in a normal copulation with their mates. The potential payoff from these one-minute stands is huge: if successful in fertilising an egg, another male will rear the unfaithful male's offspring for him.

Make love not war? For a penguin, making love is war.

There is a potential downside to all these carnal capers. Males must invest hugely in the incubation and care of young. If females have sperm from two or more males floating around their reproductive tracts, how can a male ensure that he is not wasting all his energies rearing someone else's offspring? Darwin would not be pleased! So males behave in ways that minimize that happening (see: *Sperm Competition*, p.70).

'... and if you can't be with the one you love, Honey, love the one you're with.'

(Photo: Lloyd Spencer Davis)

Eventually after two weeks or so of unadulterated sex and adultery, the female will lay a clutch of two eggs, usually about three days apart (except for King and Emperor penguins, which lay just the one). What Crosby, Stills, Nash and Young neglected to mention about 'loving the one you're with' is that, afterwards, there are the fruits of that love to contend with.

4

The Fruits of Love

'Juliet, when we made love you used to cry
You said I love you like the stars above, I'll love you till I die
There's a place for us, you know the movie song
When you gonna realise it was just that the time was wrong?'

Romeo and Juliet
Dire Straits

Penguins are their own worst enemies. We tend to think of penguins as victims. Victims of the cold. Victims of leopard seals. Victims of skuas. That is because these are the images that we are shown. Penguins hunkered down in a snowstorm, breeding in conditions where we couldn't even begin to imagine how to survive let alone rear a family. Penguins being torn apart by leopard seals. Penguin chicks being harassed by skuas.

South polar skuas on the prowl.

(Photo: G Court)

However, the weather kills relatively few penguins: they are so well insulated that they can take the worst the environment can throw at them. Real though their fear may be of leopard seals, probably less than two percent of adult penguins actually succumb to seal bites in any given breeding season. And while at times killer birds like skuas and giant petrels can take large proportions of the eggs and chicks, very often the greatest risk to eggs and chicks comes from their parents.

It is all a matter of timing. Like bad comedy, bad parenting results from inappropriate timing. For many penguin pairs, the difference between success and failure turns out to be 'just that the time was wrong'. It is the price they pay for cross-dressing as fish.

For the embryos to develop, eggs must be kept warm. Young chicks, also, are incapable of maintaining a constant body temperature by themselves. Equally, an unattended egg or young chick would be an easy target for a predator. Hence, irrespective of the number of lives the weather and predators may claim, they are still a threat. Parents must take turns, alternating attendance at the nest with periods of feeding at

A chick hatching.

(Photo: Lloyd Spencer Davis)

sea, so that one of them is always with the eggs and young chicks to protect them. And this is where the problem of timing lies.

The parent that is on the nest cannot stay there indefinitely. Parents must co-ordinate their pattern of nest attendance in such a way that the one at sea gets enough time feeding to recharge its own energy reserves but gets back to the nest before the sitting bird exhausts its reserves. If not, the bird on the nest will desert and the season will have been a failure for both: their eggs will be killed by exposure to the elements, if skuas and the like do not get them first.

The time a feeding penguin needs to be away from the nest is related to how far it must travel to get its food. This is where the costs of giving up flying become most apparent. Penguins cannot cover large distances as quickly as, say, petrels or albatross. For inshore-feeding species like the Galapagos, African, Humboldt and Yellow-eyed penguins, which feed on fish within a few kilometres of the shore, this is not much of a problem: they rarely need to go away from the nest for more than a day or two. However, many species feed a long way offshore, especially during the incubation period, travelling tens if not hundreds of kilometres to find food. These offshore foragers can be away from the nest for weeks at a time. The timing of their return is most critical: too late and the mate will have deserted. Consequently, desertions are much more common in offshore-feeding species than inshore ones (although, even in inshore species, if a partner is away for much longer than normal, it can lead to desertions).

Humboldt penguins returning to the shore in the evening.
(Photo: Lloyd Spencer Davis)

Daddy's Milk

Emperor penguins have the most extreme pattern of parenting of all. To begin with, they breed during the Antarctic winter in darkness, in temperatures that can fall below minus 60 degrees Celsius, in wind speeds that can exceed 200 kilometres per hour. If that were not bad enough, the male Emperor must go without food for over three months in these conditions.

Firstly, they must make a trek across the frozen sea ice to the breeding 'grounds'. Actually they breed on the frozen sea ice, usually in the lee of cliffs that can afford them a little protection from winds cold enough to castrate brass elephants. Courtship then takes about one month, before the female transfers the single egg to the male's waiting feet. She then waddles away across the sea-ice, leaving the male to incubate the egg for the entire incubation period. Two months. Combined with the period the male has been unable to eat during the courtship period, this means fasting for up to three-and-a-half months! Some diet. During this time the males will lose a third of their body weight and it would seem critical for the newly hatched chick that its mother should return about the time of hatching. Indeed it is, and Emperor chicks will die of starvation if their mothers dawdle on the return journey. But the chicks have one piece of insurance against starvation that other penguins don't have and it comes from a most unlikely source.

Despite having last eaten so long ago that the taste of fish and squid can be but a distant memory, Emperor penguin fathers are able to feed their new chicks on a type of milk that they manufacture by breaking down their own body tissues. Clearly, given that the male has already run its energy reserves dangerously low, there cannot be a lot where that comes from, but it can make the difference between living and dying for the Emperor penguin chick. Emperor penguin dads get my vote for 'Father of the Year' every year!

Father of the Year.

(Photo: Lloyd Spencer Davis)

But the problem of timing does not end there. While taking too long at sea can lead to desertions and the loss of eggs, later on it can claim the lives of chicks through starvation. In all species of penguin, once the chicks hatch they must be fed immediately and frequently. For offshore foragers, this means switching over to short feeding trips and making sure that the parent at sea returns to the nest about the time the chicks hatch. This is necessary because the parent on the nest, if it has been there for much more than a day, will not have any undigested food left in its belly to regurgitate to a chick. Remnants of the egg's yolk sac, which the chicks retain within their bellies, give them a bit of insurance against the late arrival of their first meal (see also: *Daddy's Milk*, p.78). However, that insurance is only good for a day or two, and many chicks die within the first week of hatching simply because they have never been fed. The parent at sea has failed to return.

In most instances, these late parents eventually return to an empty nest, proving that they are, indeed, alive and that it was just their timing that was wrong. *O Romeo,*[13] *when you gonna realise?*

[13] In Adelie penguins, it is most often the male that is late. However, this varies from species to species, and depends upon which parent is on a feeding trip just before hatching occurs.

Actually, many do realise. While a good many eggs and chicks are lost to desertion and starvation, most penguin pairs do manage to get their timing right. It seems that penguins possess an internal clock, more Timex than Rolex perhaps, but nevertheless accurate enough that it can tell them when they should head back to the nest (see: *Biological Clocks*, p.82).

A Little penguin feeds two demanding chicks almost as big as itself. *(Photo: M Renner)*

In a sense, the hatching of their chicks signals that the real work has only just begun for the parents. The parents' job is to carry food from the sea as fast as possible to the ever-hungry mouths of their cheeping chicks. This task is made distinctly more difficult by their inability to fly. For this reason, penguins can only breed successfully in areas where high concentrations of food are available close inshore for at least part of the breeding season. Breeding is timed so that the period when chicks need to be fed coincides with the maximum availability of food.

Of course, there must have been some evolutionary advantage to giving up flight, otherwise it would have been unlikely to occur. For penguins, this meant being able to dive deeper and for longer, making available concentrations of food that albatross and petrels can only dream about. In the tropics and temperate regions this means vast schools of tiny fish like anchovies and sprat. In the sub-Antarctic, fish are supplemented by dense swarms of squid and krill, components of the zooplankton. While in the Antarctic, krill dominates the diets of penguins.

Their prey would need to go very deep to get beyond the reach of the penguins. All penguins, with the exception of the Little penguin, can dive to well over 100 metres. Diving depth and duration are related to body size (in simple terms, how long you can hold your breath is a function of the size of your oxygen stores, which are related to your volume), so that in this arena the Emperor reigns supreme: the record dive for an Emperor penguin is over 500 metres!

Biological Clocks

I have a dog. Her name is Tess. She is a black labrador. Tess used to sleep on a sheepskin on the floor at the foot of my bed. She no longer sleeps there and this is why.

My wife is a nurse and when she is working an 'early shift' we need to set the alarm for 6.00 am. However, Tess would always jump onto the bed and wake me at about five minutes to six. As anyone who has had a labrador will know, they will do absolutely anything for food and, as I give Tess a dog biscuit for breakfast every morning, it is easy to appreciate why she should be so anxious to wake me. Indeed, had she acted so when the alarm went off, all would be unremarkable: it would simply be another case of Pavlov's dogs. Bell rings, dog salivates, reward is given.

While there is no doubt that Tess was being conditioned to wake me

An Adelie penguin rushes home.

(Photo: Lloyd Spencer Davis)

by the reward of a dog biscuit, what made this remarkable was that she was able to anticipate when the alarm should go off, and to do that she must have had her own internal clock. Animals have biological clocks because the consequences of performing behaviours can vary considerably depending upon when a behaviour is performed. Had Tess jumped upon my bed at midday it would have produced no effect at all in terms of getting a biscuit, and had she jumped on me at midnight it would have certainly produced an effect, but not the desired one!

Now in this instance, I was going to be getting up anyway; was five minutes lost sleep and a faceful of dog saliva really enough to banish her from the bedroom forever? Probably, but the real problem was that Tess still insisted on jumping on the bed at 5.55 am even on those mornings when the alarm was not set. Typically my wife worked for five days followed by a variable number of days off. For Tess to have had any chance of being allowed to continue to sleep in our bedroom she would have needed to be able to count five days from the morning the alarm first went off and then cease jumping on me until the cycle began again. Either such an interval timer was beyond her or she chose to wake me anyway on the off chance that I would get her a biscuit. Penguins, however, possess just such an interval timer and it allows them to measure the incubation period of their eggs.

Why might that be important to them? While parents can afford to be away from the nest for several days or even weeks during incubation, once their chicks hatch they must be able to feed them regularly and frequently. Parents at sea will stop feeding and head back to the nest if their chicks are about to hatch. Exactly how they know hatching is imminent is unclear, but it seems to involve an interval timer.

In principle, it probably works a lot like setting an oven timer to bake a cake. An event must occur to set the timer and then, after a specified period, there needs to be an alarm bell to warn that the cake is cooked or, in this case, the eggs are done. All animals possess biological clocks which produce rhythms in the body's hormones and it seems likely that any internal timer will also be hormonally-based. Setting of the timer probably occurs at the time of laying when the birds stop copulating, causing their reproductive organs to regress faster than any cold shower could. As a result, levels of testosterone and oestrogens, the reproductive hormones that control sex drives, fall precipitously, effectively acting as a signal to start the timer. But what could function as the alarm bell to tell a foraging penguin that its eggs are ready? Some evidence suggests that levels of another hormone, progesterone, rise just before hatching. Whether this really is the trigger to get penguins to return requires more research.

Penguins, like Tess, can tell the time; but unlike Tess, they can also measure intervals and this is vitally important to the survival of their chicks. Consequently, as far as I'm concerned, there will always be a place for penguins at the foot of my bed.

However, perhaps the last word on this should belong to Tess: any dog that can eat my wife's $300 Swiss watch, then excrete it on the bathroom floor and live to tell the tale, knows more about the passage of time and its effects on survival than I can ever hope to understand.

Lawbreakers

Physics has laws, biology has probabilities. Despite the more uncertain nature of biological systems, there is one aspect of bird behaviour that is so close to being a law that it seems animals should be fined for breaking it. It governs clutch size in birds and was originally proposed by David Lack, a British ornithologist. Lack's 'law' states that the clutch size of birds should correspond to the maximum number of chicks they can rear. However, all the crested penguins – those with the well-endowed eyebrows – flaunt such rules:

- They lay two eggs but only ever rear one chick.
- The second egg is larger than the first: amongst other birds the last-laid egg may sometimes be smaller, but never larger.
- The size differences between the eggs are the largest for any birds, with the second egg being up to twice the size of the first.
- The interval between laying the first and second egg, about six days, is the longest for any penguin, and amongst the longest for any bird.
- Despite the long laying interval, the chick from the second-laid egg hatches first.
- In three species of crested penguins (Fiordland, Snares and Rockhopper) both chicks typically hatch but the smaller chick from the late-hatching first egg is unable to compete with its sibling for food and dies of starvation.
- In the other two species of crested penguins (Erect-crested, and Macaroni/Royal), they typically lose the first egg before or on the day the second egg is laid. There is even some suggestion that parents may deliberately eject the first egg, although in my experience, it is most usually lost through neglect.

Erect-crested penguin eggs: the first-laid egg is on the left. *(Photo: Lloyd Spencer Davis)*

Diet studies and attempts to track the movements of crested penguins at sea using transmitters all indicate that they are offshore feeders. It seems unlikely that they could transport enough food back from such faraway distances to support two chicks. So why lay two eggs? Some have suggested that crested penguins are actually at an evolutionary halfway house, where they are in the process of reducing their clutch size down to one, like Emperor or King penguins. But this does not explain why they should reduce the size of the first egg rather than simply not laying the second egg. Others have suggested having another egg acts as a form of insurance in case one egg or chick is lost. This potentially might have some relevance for those species that routinely hatch two chicks but the first egg cannot be much insurance in species where it is lost or even chucked out of the nest before the second is laid.

The obligatory brood reduction and egg-size differences of crested penguins remains a mystery. It awaits a scientific Mrs Marples to solve it. Until then, all David Lack can say is that the clutch size of birds *probably* corresponds to the maximum number of chicks they can rear.

However, penguins are visual feeders, meaning that they use their eyes to locate their prey. The deeper they go, the darker it gets. While the bioluminescence of some squid probably aids their capture, fortunately for penguins, many squid and krill undergo daily vertical migrations, coming closer to the surface as the light levels lessen. While penguins are capable of feeding at over 100 metres, most feeding takes the form of repeated diving to depths considerably less than this. Even so, it is a feat that flying birds could never hope to emulate.

Typically, food in sufficient quantities to feed chicks is only available for a certain period of the year and latitude affects the duration of that period. This restricts the time available for breeding the closer to the South Pole that penguins breed. Although the season is shorter in the Antarctic, massive plankton blooms and 24-hour daylight mean that the parents can forage around the clock.

The amount of food parents deliver to their chicks depends upon how far they need to swim to get it. Penguins feeding close inshore with a reliable food supply typically can rear two chicks. For those feeding farther offshore (e.g. Magellanic,

Adelie, Chinstrap), whether they can physically transport enough food back for two chicks will depend upon how abundant and accessible food is in a particular year. Crested penguins forage even farther afield, and although they always lay two eggs, they never rear more than one chick (see: *Lawbreakers*, p.84). There is no way that the two largest species of penguins, Emperors and Kings, could ever bring back enough food for two of their big chicks, so they don't even try: they lay just a single egg. Even then, it is a struggle for Emperors and Kings to fatten up the chick to full size in the time available. Emperors only manage to do so by beginning breeding in the winter, leaving the chicks with the whole summer to increase their waistlines. King penguins adopt a different approach and spread breeding over more than one year. Taking about 14 months to rear their chicks, they can breed only twice every three years. In the process they push the dividing line between parental care and neglect to new extremes (see: *Home Alone*, p.87).

Naturally, the amount of food that must be brought back for the chicks increases as they get older and bigger. At a certain point, the chicks' needs can no longer be satisfied by

Mutant teddy bear? *(Photo: Lloyd Spencer Davis)*

Home Alone

Penguins have an image of being cute and cuddly. But as anyone who has handled a penguin can tell you, they are tough and ornery. Their feathers are short and stiff. Their bodies muscular and powerful. I have seen grown men knocked down by a single blow from an Emperor penguin's flipper. Cute maybe, cuddly: never. Except, perhaps, for the chicks of King penguins, which look like mutant teddy bears.

The King penguin is a large bird, about 15 kilograms in its underwear. It takes one heck of a lot of fish and squid to get their chicks up to anywhere near adult size, and the parents are unable to accomplish the task within the summer breeding season. As a consequence, chicks are left by themselves during the winter months while the parents go off in search of food, sometimes covering thousands of kilometres in the process. The chicks must go without food for months at a time: in the most extreme cases they go for up to five months between meals!

Incredible! You've gotta love them, for their tenacity if not their cuddly appearance.

having just one parent foraging and both parents must go to sea simultaneously to hunt for food. This means leaving the chicks unguarded. It is not something the parents do lightly. They will continue to guard their chicks for as long as possible, with the length of the guard stage being influenced by a combination of the food demands made by the chicks, the distance parents must travel to get food, and the availability of food. Parents leave their chicks alone at a younger age when: they must feed two chicks (compared to parents with just a single chick), breed in locations where they must forage farther offshore, and in years when food supply is poor.

In most species, the chicks are left alone between two to four weeks of age. By this time they are capable of regulating their own body temperature, recognising their parents' voices, and recognising their own nest site. Important attributes if they are to be able to survive by themselves and reunite with their parents. Just like adults, the chicks use the nest site as the focus for any rendezvous, and both parent and chick recognise each other from their calls. Nevertheless, for those penguins breeding in the open (the Antarctic and sub-Antarctic penguins), the post-guard stage leaves the

Adelie penguin chicks congregate in crèches.
(Photo: Lloyd Spencer Davis)

chicks potentially exposed to both predators and inclement weather. The chicks of these species often congregate together in crèches, a sort of penguin version of kindergarten. The crèche affords them some security in numbers and perhaps provides another warm body to cuddle up to if the weather should turn nasty. Crèches are not, however, the shining example of altruistic togetherness that they seemed to be to the early Antarctic explorers.

Levick, a biologist who accompanied Captain Robert Falcon Scott to the Antarctic in 1910, presumed that when chicks became mixed up together in a crèche, the adults took collective responsibility for looking after the assembled mass of chicks. As appealing as such an image may be to our human hearts, on the contrary, Natural Selection tends to reward the selfish. Parents that wasted resources feeding chicks that were not their own would leave fewer offspring than those that put all their efforts into rearing only their own chicks. Genes controlling selfish behaviour will almost always flourish relative to any that might result in altruistic behaviour. Banding both chicks and adults has demonstrated that even after chicks join a crèche, they continue to be fed only by their own parents (see: *Crèches and Feeding Chases*, p.92). While adult penguins often stand around the outside of a crèche and may well chase predators like skuas away from themselves (thereby providing passive protection for chicks within their vicinity), they rarely interfere with predators killing chicks outside their personal space. It can be a cruel world when it comes time for a chick to stand on its own two feet.

As the chicks get older they must change into the feather

An Adelie chick in need of a haircut.
(Photo: Lloyd Spencer Davis)

survival suits that will eventually allow them to go and get their own food. Their down is progressively replaced by feathers growing underneath. Usually the last patch of down to disappear is on the top of their heads, so as they assemble on the beaches in anticipation of their first swim they resemble adolescents rebelling against a Headmaster's directive to 'get a haircut'. The chicks are in a race against time to complete their growth and to moult before conditions deteriorate at season's end. As with the age at which they were first left alone, the age at which the chicks are ready to go out on their

Crèches and Feeding Chases

There are not too many animals that will abandon their young while the parents go off to work, entrusting their flesh and blood into the care of a collective grouping known as a crèche. Humans do it. Flamingos do it. Eider ducks do it. And, most notably, some penguins do it.

Strictly speaking, a crèche is a congregation of three or more chicks. In practice, the groupings are usually larger, depending upon the size of the chicks' sub-colony

and the distribution of nests within it. At first it was believed that chicks formed crèches as a means of keeping warm. But by two weeks of age, the earliest age at which chicks are usually left alone, the chicks are already able to regulate their own body temperature and only in the most severe weather do they seek shelter from a storm by huddling together. Chicks crèche it seems mainly for protection. In fact, if there are plenty of non-breeding adults hanging about the colony, the chicks may not crèche at all. In species like the Adelie penguin, birds that were unsuccessful at breeding return to the colony about the time that the chicks are left unguarded by their parents. This influx of adult birds into the colony is known as the Reoccupation Period. Its coincidence with the beginning of the crèching stage is fortunate for the chicks, as the mere presence of the adults deters predators like skuas. Later, the number of adults in the colony dwindles towards season's end and the propensity to crèche increases, as does the size of crèches, with chicks from more than one sub-colony moving together.

Having their chicks mixed up with a lot of others creates a potential dilemma for parents when they return from the sea to feed their chicks. Fortunately, by about two weeks of age both parent and chick can recognise each other by their calls. The parent returns to the nest site and, if its chicks are not already waiting there, calls its chicks. The chicks detach themselves from the crèche and come running. Often they will be accompanied by other chicks, ever hopeful of a free meal – but the latter soon lose interest when the parent bird gives them nothing but pecks if it does not recognise their call.[14]

While parents can recognise their own chicks, all the evidence indicates that they cannot distinguish between their chicks if they have two. The chicks behave selfishly and, if there is a size difference between them, the larger one can muscle the smaller one out of the way. This can eventually lead to the smaller chick dying of starvation or growing more slowly with limited prospects of survival. From the parents' perspective, each one of their offspring is equally valuable to them. They can counteract size disparities to some extent by not incubating the first egg properly until the second egg is laid, resulting in both chicks hatching closer together than they would have otherwise. Unable to distinguish their chicks, some parents have developed an ingenious means of distributing food that tilts the balance towards the smallest chick.

When approached by its begging chicks, an Adelie, Chinstrap or Gentoo parent will turn and flee. The chicks chase after the parent, seeming to harass it. After a few metres the parent will turn and regurgitate into the mouth closest to it (usually the mouth of the largest chick). It then turns and runs again, repeating the process. Because the largest chick will sometimes fall behind, become satiated and less motivated to run, or simply get lost in the chase: almost inevitably this leads to the smallest chick also managing to get a share of the food too. In cases where the parent has only a single chick there is less need for the chick to run for its supper and feeding chases may be short or even non-existent.

[14] There have been isolated observations of adult penguins feeding chicks that were not their own, but for the most part parents do not feed other chicks no matter how much they beg.

Running for its supper. *(Photo: Lloyd Spencer Davis)*

A harried parent feeds its chick. *(Photo: Lloyd Spencer Davis)*

own will be influenced by the number of mouths their parents must feed, how far their parents must travel to get food, and how plentiful the food is once they get there. Chicks take longer to fledge if their parents must feed two chicks, if they have to travel a long way for food, or if it is a poor year for food. But they cannot afford to take too long. Eventually time will run out. *O Romeo, when you gonna realise?*

The chicks gather at the water's edge, seemingly trying to build up the courage to take the plunge. They may make one or two false starts, scrambling and squawking to get back on shore after the first sensation of being wet. At last, amid calls to each other, a group will head out to sea. Head out into the unknown. Transformed from bird to fish. At first they seem unable to accept this, keeping their heads above the water. But quickly they learn that they can go underwater. They are swimmers. They are divers.

The tragedy for penguins is that their virtuoso diving abilities have come at a price. If they *are* victims, then the blows have been self inflicted: literally wrought by their own flippers. By becoming flightless, they have made themselves vulnerable – in more ways than one.

5

Lost Souls?

'And did they get you to trade your heroes for ghosts?
Hot ashes for trees? Hot air for a cold breeze?
Cold comfort for change? And did you exchange
a walk-on part in the war for a lead role in a cage?'

Wish You Were Here
Pink Floyd

Natural Selection is war. Animals compete in a battle where the only prize is to survive. In this struggle for survival any modification that provides an advantage will proliferate. Penguins, when they gave up flight for the riches in the sea, gained an advantage. But in doing away with their wings, they passed a point of no return. They can never go back to being flyers. In a way, they have become prisoners of their early success, locked in an evolutionary cage from which there is no way out.

Their ability to dive may be the key to bountiful underwater food for both themselves and their chicks, but their aquatic lifestyle and inability to fly exact many costs. The feather survival suits that keep them warm and dry in the water must be replaced after the rigours of the breeding season. Moult is a debilitating process. Unable to feed, unable to regulate their body temperature efficiently, yet required to manufacture a brand new suit of feathers, the energy demands on the penguins are immense. To prepare for the trauma of moult, penguins go to sea immediately after breeding and spend several weeks fattening up.[15] Then they stand immobile and ragged on some desolate shore, conserving their

[15] Galapagos penguins are unusual in that they moult before breeding. This species is resident year-round and can breed several times during a single year. For them, what is before and what is after becomes a little academic.

Immobile and ragged:
a Snares penguin moults.
(Photo: M Renner)

energy as best they can to devote as much of it as possible to making feathers. During this time they lose a huge amount of body weight as they literally dine on their fat reserves. Some die. Either unable to lay down enough fat to sustain themselves through the moult or unable to complete moult before the weather deteriorates and winter sets in.

Even for those that survive, the prospects ahead are not easy. Most penguins are unable to stay at their breeding grounds all year round. One of the main advantages of flight is that it provides a fast and efficient means of migration, permitting birds to exploit breeding areas that could not sustain them at other times. Migration is daunting enough for a flying bird, but when faced with the prospect of swimming all the way, it must seem downright life-threatening. And it is. In some species nearly a quarter of the adults fail to complete their over-winter migration. For chicks, the prognosis is even worse. When chicks eventually take to the water for their first swim, they must embark on a post-fledging migration that can take from one to several years. Typically, fewer than half the chicks will survive to return to the colony as breeders, and in some instances, virtually none will.

Despite migration mortality having the single biggest impact on penguin populations, scientists know very little about where penguins go and what they do during the migration. Advances in electronic technology mean that the movements of penguins at sea can now be monitored using tiny transmitters or computers glued to their feathers. These can also record aspects of behaviour like diving depths, swimming speeds and whether the penguin is in or out of the water, as well as environmental variables such as temperature and salinity. The information is either stored on a computer chip for downloading when the penguin returns or transmitted to orbiting satellites. Neither method is without its problems. While special glues and tapes can adequately hold devices to feathers for a few weeks or even a few months, scientists have yet to solve how to maintain these attachments for the eight months or so required to track the penguins during the whole migration. Attached devices can also upset the flow of water around the penguins' bodies, creating drag and requiring more energy from the penguins to swim and dive. Streamlining the shape of the device and attaching it at the base of the back reduces this disturbance to a minimum.

Preliminary evidence from penguins tracked by satellites illustrates that they are capable of covering prodigious distances on their over-winter swims. Migration paths of Adelie penguins breeding on Ross Island, Antarctica, demonstrate that they must travel at least 5,500 kilometres: a long way to swim for fish or fowl!

But there is no escaping that the evolutionary path of penguins, if not the migratory one, has made them vulnerable. Doubly vulnerable. Not only must they contend with the limitations of being flightless and the threats from predators, but the likelihood of their eggs being deserted or their chicks dying of starvation will be gravely affected by anything that increases the time they must spend at sea feeding.

Despite these downsides, it is clear that the original trade penguins made – wings for flippers – was a good one. Fifty millions years or so is a long time in anyone's book. Penguins have been on Earth for ten times longer than humans and our ancestors. And therein lies a huge irony.

Penguins evolved on isolated predator-free islands where for most of their existence, they could prosper without wings. Importantly, these islands were not just predator-free, but also human-free. Penguins are now discovering their real enemy, and that enemy is us.

We've even dabbled in a little predation ourselves. During the last 200 years penguins have been killed in their thousands for their skins and boiled down to extract the oil from their bodies. We've harvested their eggs. Thirteen million eggs were taken from African penguins in one area alone over a 30-year period. In the Falkland Islands, an annual harvest takes place every 9 November, where people gather up the eggs of Rockhopper penguins by the barrow load. The harvest is regulated now but, even so, each year 10,000 eggs remain destined to become giant omelettes. However, we have been most lethal by acting as the agents for things that kill. We have introduced exotic predators such as stoats and cats to the isolated parts of the world where penguins breed, decimating whole populations almost overnight.

We kill penguins in other ways too. If it's not predators it's disease. When hundreds of penguin chicks died in Antarctica, the chief suspect was avian malaria contracted from chicken that researchers were eating. We can even kill penguins with kindness. The unintentional disturbance associated

Yellow-eyed penguins that have succumbed to biotoxins resulting from human-induced changes to their marine environment.
(Photo: J Darby)

with getting too close to breeding penguins by otherwise well-meaning visitors to Antarctica can cause distress and breeding failure. On Macquarie Island, seven thousand King penguins were reported to have died after being killed in a stampede induced by a low-flying aircraft.

Indirectly, too, penguins experience interference at the hands of humans. By overfishing, we have made it more difficult for parents to find food, increasing the level of breeding failures. By polluting the oceans we have made them

The Real Oil on the World's Biggest Seabird Rescue

The Maximum Security Prison on Robben Island has a concrete cell that housed prisoner 488/64 for over 18 years. It is barely big enough for a bed and the only view through its barred window is of a concrete courtyard. Nelson Mandela was imprisoned there for his vision – a vision of a black South Africa coexisting in harmony with a white South Africa. How ironic, then, that while the prison walls temporarily blocked his view, they could not shield him from the sound of a bird that, in a way, symbolized the new South Africa that he would eventually oversee.

Part black, part white, the African penguin is renowned for its donkey-like braying. So much so, that sometimes it is called the Jackass penguin. Nearly 6,000 pairs of African penguins breed on Robben Island, almost within braying distance of Cape Town (making it the third-largest colony for the species), and amidst one of the busiest shipping lanes in the world. It is a disaster just waiting to happen. Unfortunately for the penguins, the wait is never likely to be long.

On 20 June 1994, a freighter carrying iron ore, the *Apollo Sea*, sank north of Robben Island, releasing about 2,000 tons of fuel oil into the sea. Oil may be good for powering a ship, but it is a death sentence for penguins that swim through it. Their feathers get clogged, destroying their waterproofing. An oiled penguin is unable to stay in the water. While there may be toxic effects of the oil in severe cases, for the rest: if hypothermia does not get them, starvation will. About 10,000 penguins were affected by oil from the *Apollo Sea*, but worse was yet to come.

Six years later, on 23 June 2000, another iron ore ship, the *Treasure*, sank 20 kilometres north of Robben Island with 1,300 tons of fuel oil onboard. Two days later oil washed ashore on Robben Island and 1,350 oiled penguins were picked up by the Southern African National Foundation for the Conservation of Coastal Birds (SANCCOB) and transported to a warehouse on the mainland where they were washed by hand to clean the oil from their feathers. By 28 June, oil had surrounded Dassen Island, about 30 kilometres north of where the *Treasure* sank and home to the largest colony of African penguins in the world. Estimates suggested that 20 percent of all African penguins were likely to be oiled. At one stage SANCCOB had approximately 12 percent of the global population of the species in a single warehouse. By the time the disaster had been played out, SANCCOB and 40,000 volunteers would catch 43,000 penguins from Robben and Dassen Islands. Remarkably, the treatment was very effective and fewer than 1,000 birds taken into captivity died.

Unoiled penguins were fenced in on Robben Island (and Dassen) to prevent them going to sea and becoming oiled: the home of one of the world's most notorious jails had become a prison for penguins too. While the capacity of penguins to fast for long periods meant that they could remain fenced for several days without being fed, there was a limit to how long they could be confined. A decision was taken to transport 5,000 unoiled penguins from Robben Island and a further 12,500 from Dassen Island to Port Elizabeth on South Africa's south-eastern coast where they were

Oil spills exact a heavy toll on penguins. *(Photo: PD Boersma)*

released into the sea. It was expected that they would use their excellent navigation abilities to swim back to the islands, but that it would take them about two weeks to get there, by which time it was hoped the oil would be cleaned up. Satellite transmitters were attached to three penguins: 'Peter' from Robben Island and 'Percy' and 'Pamela' from Dassen Island. Peter, released on 30 June, waddled up the beach at Robben Island on 18 July, managing to just beat Percy home.

It is only a matter of time before the next oil spill, if not near Robben Island, then near another penguin colony. And it would be naïve to expect that there will always be a SANCCOB, thousands of volunteers and the huge infrastructure needed to rescue penguins. On 16 January 2001 the *Jessica* ran aground in the Galapagos Islands, releasing an oil slick that potentially threatened the unique wildlife in the area, including one of the world's most endangered penguins, the Galapagos penguin. Fortunately, strong currents and wind eventually took most of the oil offshore. Which is just as well, because there was precious little the islanders could have done.

Peter has begun breeding again on Robben Island, his life spared for now. But in a sense he is still a prisoner, still at our mercy. From his nest it is possible to see the ships continuing to pass by, the skyline of Cape Town beyond, and the threat of death by oil spill hanging over him like a sentence.

I wonder if at night he listens for Nelson Mandela in the distance?

less hospitable places for penguins. Oil spills in Australia, South Africa and South America have exacted heavy tolls and involved massive clean-up operations.

We destroy the habitat penguins need to breed. Deforestation in New Zealand almost eliminated the Yellow-eyed penguin from the shores of the mainland. Humboldt penguins often make their breeding burrows in guano, the nitrogenous wastes that build up over many years in breeding colonies of boobies, cormorants and pelicans; but in Peru, even now, this guano is harvested for its nutrients, putting at risk the nesting of the penguins.

Perhaps the most sinister threat to penguins from Humankind is the one most difficult to control: global warming. Industrial pollution in the Northern Hemisphere manifests itself in the Southern Hemisphere as warm water events like El Niño. For penguins this can be devastating. Warm water suppresses the up-welling of nutrient-rich cold water, which is needed to fuel the planktonic blooms on which the penguins prey and, ultimately, the penguins themselves depend. No up-welling means no food. Already there have been catastrophic crashes in penguin populations associated with

Global Warming and Krill

To survive in the Antarctic, penguins like the Adelie, Chinstrap and Gentoo need the winters to be really cold. As counter-intuitive as that may seem, it is because the continuing presence of their staple food depends upon a cold so frightful that it can cause the top layer of the sea to freeze completely.

The diet of these penguins is made up almost exclusively of krill. Krill are tiny crustaceans that look like miniature rock lobsters. They are paid-up members of the zooplankton, occurring in dense swarms within the Antarctic waters. For such tiny animals they are capable of living for many years. However, most juvenile krill do not survive their first Antarctic winter and, therefore, do not reach reproductive maturity. The baby krill spend the dark winter months nestled up against the underside of the sea-ice. And here's the paradox: to survive the cold, they need it to be really cold – because only in the severest winters is the ice thick enough to insulate them from the harsh Antarctic conditions.

Such severe winters occur in a cyclical pattern – about once every seven years – which is related to the rotating pattern of sea water currents. Krill get bigger as they age. Diet samples taken from penguins show that the average length of krill they eat increases each year for about six years and then, suddenly, goes back to the smallest size. That is, these penguins depend upon a single group of adult krill that survived their first winter together until the next harsh winter permits another group of baby krill to reach adulthood. The unfortunate thing from the penguins' perspective is that krill do not live forever. Seven years or so is about it. Enter the problem of global warming.

The emission of greenhouse gases and the like by an industrialised Northern Hemisphere has, during the last half of the Twentieth Century, raised ambient temperatures even in Antarctica. As a consequence, the cycle of winters with heavy sea ice has been suppressed. Without such conditions, few krill can reach adulthood and the stock of adults has begun to dwindle. Already this is having a dramatic effect on the breeding success of penguins around the Antarctic Peninsula.

Chaos theorists love to cite the notion of a butterfly flapping its wings on one part of the globe eventually causing a storm on another. But a BMW being driven along a European autobahn causing a penguin chick to starve to death in Antarctica: now that's chaos!

Gentoo penguins breeding on the Antarctic Peninsula need a good supply of krill to feed their chicks. (Photo: R Cuthbert)

Yellow-eyed penguins march to an uncertain future. *(Photo: G Court)*

El Niño reported from the Galapagos Islands, New Zealand, and the sub-Antarctic Islands. And these events appear to be becoming more frequent. For those penguins breeding in Antarctica, global warming has even more significance (see: *Global Warming and Krill*, p.107).

Sadly for these birds that would be fish, their fate rests in our hands. We are both sinner and potential saviour. Whether penguins survive for another 50 million years, or even another 50 years, is going to be largely up to us. The loss of flight has left them vulnerable. Ultimately it will be our actions that determine whether penguins have won the war or simply become, like the song says, 'lost souls swimming in a fish bowl'.

How I wish – how I wish you were here.

Penguins breeding in Antarctica have reason to fear global warming.
(Photo: Lloyd Spencer Davis)

Index

Page numbers in **bold** indicate photographs.